SECONDARY
SCHOOL
MATHEMATICS 4

SENIOR DIVISION

NOTES

COLES EDITORIAL BOARD

Bound to stay open

Publisher's Note

Otabind (Ota-bind). This book has been bound using the patented Otabind process. You can open this book at any page, gently run your finger down the spine, and the pages will lie flat.

ABOUT COLES NOTES

COLES NOTES have been an indispensible aid to students on five continents since 1948.

COLES NOTES are available for a wide range of individual literary works. Clear, concise explanations and insights are provided along with interesting interpretations and evaluations.

Proper use of COLES NOTES will allow the student to pay greater attention to lectures and spend less time taking notes. This will result in a broader understanding of the work being studied and will free the student for increased participation in discussions.

COLES NOTES are an invaluable aid for review and exam preparation as well as an invitation to explore different interpretive paths.

COLES NOTES are written by experts in their fields. It should be noted that any literary judgement expressed herein is just that – the judgement of one school of thought. Interpretations that diverge from, or totally disagree with any criticism may be equally valid.

COLES NOTES are designed to supplement the text and are not intended as a substitute for reading the text itself. Use of the NOTES will serve not only to clarify the work being studied, but should enhance the readers enjoyment of the topic.

ISBN 0-7740-3777-6

© COPYRIGHT 1998 AND PUBLISHED BY
COLES PUBLISHING COMPANY
TORONTO - CANADA
PRINTED IN CANADA

Manufactured by Webcom Limited
Cover finish: Webcom's Exclusive **DURACOAT**

CONTENTS

SYMBOLS AND ABBREVIATIONS **5**

DEFINITIONS **6**

UNIT 1- RELATIONS AND FUNCTIONS **15**

UNIT 2- THE EXPOTENTIAL AND LOGARITHMIC FUNCTIONS **27**

UNIT 3- QUADRATIC FUNCTIONS AND QUADRATIC EQUATIONS **39**

UNIT 4- THE CIRCLE **51**

UNIT 5- TRIGONOMETRIC FUNCTIONS **62**

UNIT 6- SEQUENCES AND SERIES **69**

CHRISTMAS EXAMINATION **71**

EASTER EXAMINATION **75**

JUNE EXAMINATION **78**

NEW-APPROACH MATHEMATICS

These notes on the course in Mathematics for Middle School are arranged as listed by topics in the Course of Study for Grade 12 by the Ontario Department of Education.

Symbols and Abbreviations

$\because$	because	$\therefore$	therefore
...	and so on		
{ }	the set	ϕ	null set
=	equals, is equal to	$\neq$	is not equal to
$\doteq$	approximately equal to		
$\cong \equiv$	is congruent to	$\approx \mid\mid\mid$	is similar to
$\mid\mid$	is parallel to	$\mid\mid$ gm	parallelogram
+	plus, add, positive	$-$	minus, subtract, negative
$\pm$	plus or minus, positive or negative		
>	is greater than	<	is less than
$\ngtr$	is not greater than	$\nless$	is not less than
$\geq$	greater than or equal to	$\leq$	less than or equal to
$\perp$	is perpendicular to		
$\angle, \angle$'s	angle, angles		
$\angle$'d	angled		
Δ	triangle		
$\mid a \mid$	the absolute value of a	$\mid$	such that
ϵ	belongs to, is a member of	$\notin$	is not a member of
$\cup$	the union of (cup)	$\cap$	the intersection of (cap)
$\subseteq$	is a subset of	$\subset$	is a proper subset of
$\rightarrow$	the mapping symbol, implies		
$\leftrightarrow$	is equivalent to, iff, biconditional		
iff	if and only if		
$\sqrt{a}$	the square root of a	$\sqrt[n]{a}$	the nth root of a

i $i^2 = -1$

a:b:c   the ratio of a to b to c

$A \times B$ A cross B (Cartesian product)

N   the natural (counting) numbers

N_0 the natural numbers, including zero

I   the integers

Q   the rational numbers

R   the real numbers

Cl   closure property

C   commutative property

A   associative property

D   distributive property

$\sum_{p=1}^{p=30} f_p$ the series $f_1 + f_2 + f_3 + \ldots + f_{30}$

– Definitions –

absolute value — the greater of a number and its additive inverse.

acute angle — an angle whose degree measure is 0 or less than 90.

additive inverse — the number equal in value but opposite in sign to a given number.

amplitude — the perpendicular distance of a maximum point (on a sine 0 or cosine 0 curve) from the 0 axis.

angle — the union of two rays.

angle of elevation — an angle measured upward from a horizontal line of sight.

angle of depression — an angle measured downward from a horizontal line of sight.

adjacent angles — two angles having a common ray, and whose second rays are on either side of this ray.

arc	— if any two points of the circle are chosen, these two points, and all points on the circle which lie between these points form an arc.
major arc	— that arc of a circle which has, as a proper subset of its points, those points which lie in a semi-circle.
minor arc	— that arc of a circle which is a proper subset of a semi-circle.
area (of a circle)	— the union of the circle and the region enclosed by the circle.
associative property	— the property exemplified by $(a + b) + c = a + (b + c)$ where a, b, c are real numbers. Note that it may be studied under operations other than addition.
assumption	— a fact accepted without proof.
atomic sentence	— a representation of a statement of a fact which is either true or untrue. It contains no connectives such as and, or, etc.
biconditional (iff)	— the name given to the necessary and sufficient condition for a relationship to hold. It is signified usually, by the words "if and only if". (the short form for this is iff)
binary relation	— a relation existing between two variables, shown by a set of ordered pairs.
bisect	— to "cut" something in half.
bisect an angle	— to draw a ray such that its union with two rays on either side of it forms two adjacent angles of equal measure.
chord	— a line segment whose end points lie on a curve. (Eg. chord of a circle)

circumcentre	— that point, usually associated with a triangle, from which a circle may be drawn through the vertices.
circumcircle	— the circle which passes through the vertices of a rectilineal figure (usually a triangle).
circumference	- the locus traced by the rotation of the endpoint of the radius of a circle.
closure	- that property, usually associated with a set of elements, by which an operation on elements of a given set yield a unique result, the result being another member of the given set.
collinear	— points are said to be collinear if they lie in the same straight line.
commutative property	— that property which allows for the reversability of order in a given operation.
complementary angles	— angles whose measures add to 90.
concurrent	— lines or curves which share a common point.
concyclic	— the description of points which lie on the same circle.
conditional (if... then)	— a molecular sentence formed by linking two atomic sentences together by means of the connective "if... then..."
congruent	- equal in every respect, except position.
conjunctive (and)	— a molecular sentence formed by linking two atomic sentences with the connective "and".
converse	— the molecular sentence formed by reversing the hypothesis and the conclusion in a conditional sentence.
corollary	— a fact which follows immediately from some proved fact.

cyclic order	— the order which allows for elements abcd, to be placed in each of the following orders in turn: bcda, cdab, dabc, abcd,
cyclic quadrilateral	— a quadrilateral having its four vertices on the same circle.
deductive study	— the development of some fact (mathematical or otherwise) by means of a set of rules and postulates.
degree	— $\frac{1}{360}$ of a complete revolution.
diagonal	— the line segment joining any two non-adjacent vertices of a rectilineal figure.
diameter	— the chord of a circle which passes through the centre.
discriminant	— $b^2 - 4ac$ in the formula for the solutions of a quadratic equation.
disjunction (or)	— the molecular sentence formed by joining two atomic sentences with the connective "or".
distributive property	— the property linking multiplication with addition.
division	— the inverse of multiplication.
domain	— if A is a relation in two variables (x, y) then the domain is the set of all real numbers x which are the first elements of the ordered pairs in the solution set of the relation.
equilateral	— a figure (rectilineal) having its sides equal, and its angles equal.
escribed circle	— a circle associated with a triangle, which touches one side of the triangle and the other two sides produced!
function	— a set of ordered pairs generated by some defining sentence. No two first elements of a function may be identical.

hypotenuse	— that side of a right-angled triangle which is opposite the right angle.
incentre	— the centre of the inscribed circle of a triangle.
inductive method	— that method whereby a conclusion is reached, or anticipated, after experimentation rather than after rigorous proof.
inscribed circle	— that circle which touches all the sides of a given rectilineal figure.
intercept	— the signed distance from the origin, at which a curve cuts an axis.
interior (of a circle)	— the region enclosed by the circle.
(of an angle)	— the region enclosed by the angle x such that $0 \leq x < 180$.
intersection	— a point common to two straight lines — a region common to two regions — a set of elements containing all those elements and only those elements common to two or more given sets.
isosceles triangle	— a triangle having two equal sides.
line segment	— a line having a fixed measure determined by two fixed points on it.
locus	— the set of points which fulfill a given condition. — the path traced by a point moving in accordance with a given condition.
logarithm	— the exponent of a power (usually with base 10) which equals a given number.
logical connectives	— connectives used to join atomic sentences to form molecular sentences. Some connectives are and, or, if... then..., not, if and only if.

major segment (of a circle)	— that region of the disc of a circle, greater than a semicircle, bounded by the circle and a chord.
mean proportional	— an element of a set of three ordered numbers whose square is equal to the product of the other two.
measure (of an angle, line segment etc.)	— a number associated with angle, line segment etc.
minor segment	— that region of the disc of a circle less than a semicircle (see major segment).
molecular sentence	— the combination of two (or more) atomic sentences.
natural numbers	— $N = \{1, 2, 3, 4, \ldots\}$
negation	— a molecular sentence containing the word "not" to indicate that a statement is untrue.
null set	— the set having no members. This is usually designated by the Greek letter phi (ϕ).
obtuse angle	— an angle whose measure lies between $90°$ and $180°$.
one-to-one correspondence	– a comparison which associates each element of one set with one unique element of a second set.
order relation (for numerals)	— in considering the size of numbers on a number line drawn with the negative numbers to the left of zero, the order relation states that numbers to the right of zero are greater than numbers to the left. In general if $a - b > 0$ then $a > b$.
orthocentre	— the point common to the three altitudes of a triangle.
parallel lines	— lines having the same direction
	— lines which will not meet when produced for a finite distance in either direction.

12

parallelogram	— a quadrilateral having both pairs of opposite sides parallel.
parameter	— a variable such as m or b, in the equation $y = mx + b$, which is a constant or fixed number for each member of a family, but which is characteristic of the family.
perimeter	— the measure of a closed figure
period	— the length along the θ axis (in the graph of a periodic function) between two adjacent points in the same phase.
perpendicular	— one line is said to be perpendicular to another if it meets it at right angles.
polygon	— the rectilineal path enclosing a region bounded by three or more line segments.
postulate	— see assumption.
prime number	— a number greater than 1 whose only factors are 1 and itself.
pythagorean relation	— the square on the hypotenuse of a right-angled triangle is equal to the sum of the squares on the other two sides.
quadrant	— one of four regions in which a pair of axis divides the plane.
quadratic function	— a function whose defining sentence has the second power as the highest power of the variable.
quadrilateral	— a polygon having four sides
quantifier	— a word to describe such words as all, each, every, there exists, some, used in logical statements in the development of some idea.
radian	— the measure of an angle subtended at the centre of a circle by an arc equal in length to the measure of the radius.

radical	— a name frequently given to the square root symbol ($\sqrt{\ }$)
radius	— a line segment terminated at one end by the centre, and at the other by a point in the circle.
range	— the values which may be taken by a dependent variable for given values of the independent variable in a relation.
ratio	— an ordered set of numbers, not all zero.
rational number	— $Q = \{ \frac{a}{b} \mid a, b \in I, b \neq 0 \}$
ray	— that part of a line which includes a fixed point, and that part of the line lying to one side of the point.
reciprocal	— two numbers are reciprocals, one of the other, if their product is unity (1).
rectangle	— a quadrilateral having opposite sides parallel, and one of whose angles measures $90°$.
rectilineal region	— a region bounded by straight line segments.
recursion relation	— a relationship existing among the terms of a sequence by which a term is defined by the term or terms which precede it.
region	— an undefined concept referring to an area such as an angular space, or the portion of a plane enclosed by a set of points.
relation	— a set of points generated by some defining sentence.
right bisector	— a line drawn perpendicular to a given line segment, through its midpoint.
secant	— a line cutting a curve in two or more points.

sector	— the union of two radii, the arc joining the corresponding points on the circle, and the enclosed region.
segment (of a circle)	— the union of an arc, the segment joining its end points, and the enclosed region.
major segment	— the segment defined by an arc greater than a semicircle.
minor segment	— the segment defined by an arc less than a semicircle.
semicircle	— the set of points formed by the ends of a diameter and the arc on one side (or the other) of these two points.
sentence	— the representation of a statement. (the sentence holds the same relation to statement as numeral holds to number
sequence	— an ordered set of numbers 2, 4, 6
series	— the indicated sum of a sequence 2 + 4 + 6
set	— a number of elements having some common property.
solution set	— the values of a variable which satisfy a given relation or equation.
square	— a parallelogram having equal sides and having the measure of one angle 90.
subset	— none, some, or all of the elements of a given set under consideration.
subtraction	— the reverse operation to addition.
supplementary angles	— two angles whose measures have a sum of 180.
symmetry	— that property of a figure which exhibits one portion of the figure to be a mirror image of the other
	— symmetry with respect to a point exists if for any points on the figure there exists a second point collinear with the

	other two such that the given point is the midpoint of the line segment joining the two points chosen on the figure.
tangent	— the limiting position of the secant as it rotates about the point of contact.
transitive (assumption)	— for equalities if x = y and y = z then x = z for inequalities if a, b, c ϵ Q, and a > b and b > c, then a > c.
transversal	— a line intersecting two or more lines or line segments.
trapezoid	— a quadrilateral with one pair of opposite sides parallel.
triangle	— a three-sided polygon.
trichotomy property	— if a, b ϵ Q then a > b, a = b or a < b.
union	— the set containing all elements in any number of sets to be considered.
undefined terms	— these refer, in general, to ideas or concepts whose implications are best defined through usage. e.g. set, point, line, curve, plane, space.
vertex	— the fixed point common to any two adjacent sides of a polygon.

Notes on the Course of Study

The **italicized** headings are copied from the Department of Education Course of Study for Mathematics, Grade 12, Five-year Programme, All Branches.

UNIT 1: RELATIONS AND FUNCTIONS (4 WEEKS)

This unit begins with a review of several topics from various Grade 11 units dealing with the straight line and introduces the concept of the linear function.

1. Review of the development of the real number system and its properties.

16

The check marks in the following table indicate that the set of numbers shown in closed under the indicated operation.

	Addition	Subtraction	Multiplication	Division
$N = \{1, 2, 3, 4, \ldots\}$	√		√	
$N_0 = \{0, 1, 2, 3, 4, \ldots\}$	√		√	
$I = \{0, \pm 1, \pm 2, \pm 3, \ldots\}$	√	√	√	
$Q = \{\frac{a}{b} \mid a, b \in I, b \neq 0\}$	√	√	√	√
R is the union of Q and the irrationals	√	√	√	√

Fig. 1

The number sets have been developed as they are required by man to do his calculations. The need for new systems of numbers has arisen as the problems to be solved increased in complexity. The table in Fig. 1 shows an increase in the number of operations possible as the number sets become more complicated. Note that the set R allows for the same operations as Q, but, in addition, roots may be taken, and a special, useful number, π, has been included.

Properties of the Real Numbers:

Property	Addition	Multiplication
Closure	a + b is a unique number	ab is a unique real number
Commutative	a + b = b + a	ab = ba
Associative	(a + b) + c = a + (b + c)	(ab) c = a (bc)
Distributive	a (b + c) = ab + ac	
Identity element	0; a + o = a	1; a (1) = a
Inverse element	the number a, and its opposite, -a, are inverse elements a + (-a) = 0	the number a, and its reciprocal, $\frac{1}{a}$, are inverse elements $a(\frac{1}{a}) = 1$ (a ≠ 0)

Note: (1) In the above table a, b, c are real numbers

(2) Although the properties are listed under the operations addition and multiplication, they also hold for subtraction and division, which are inverse operations to addition and multiplication respectively.

Review of graphing of linear equations and inequalities in one variable.

Sample Solutions:

(i) Solve the equation $3x + 7 = -2$, $x \epsilon I$, and graph the solution set on a suitable number line.

$$3x + 7 = -2$$
$$3x = -9 \quad \text{(addition of -7)}$$
$$x = -3 \quad \text{(Division by 3)}$$

(See meaning of ⟷ in list of symbols and abbreviations)

Fig. 2

(ii) Solve the equation $|4x + 1| = 9$, $x \epsilon R$ and graph the solution set on a suitable number line.

$$|4x + 1| = 9$$

$+ (4x + 1) = 9$	or	$- (4x + 1) = 9$
$4x = 8$	or	$- 4x - 1 = 9$
$x = 2$	or	$x = -\frac{5}{2}$

Fig. 3

(iii) Solve $3x - 4 > 5$, $x \epsilon R$ and graph the solution set on a suitable number line.

$$3x - 4 > 5$$
$$3x > 9$$
$$x > 3$$

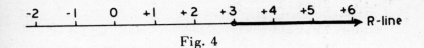

Fig. 4

(iv) Solve $|3 + x| \geq 7$, $x \epsilon$ R and graph the solution set on a suitable number line.

$$|3 + x| \geq 7$$

← $3 + x \geq 7$	or	$-3 - x \geq 7$
← $x \geq 4$	or	$x \leq -10$

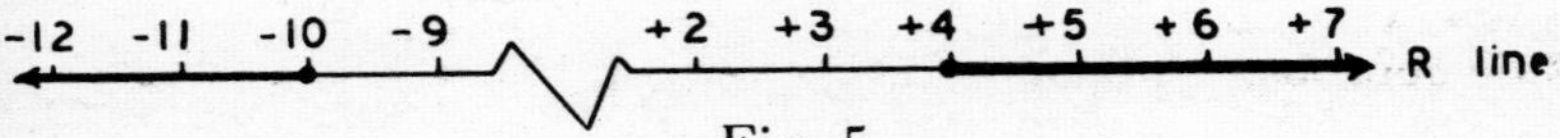

Fig. 5

Note:

(a) The above examples show detail which is usually unnecessary, but which you should understand.

(b) The graphs in (iii) and (iv) show a method of indicating that the end points are, or are not, included in the graph.

(c) In future, unless otherwise indicated, the variables are members of R.

Solutions of linear equations in one variable involving fractions

Sample solutions:

(i) $\dfrac{x + 5}{6} - \dfrac{x + 3}{4} = \dfrac{x - 1}{9}$

$6(x + 5) - 9(x + 3) = 4(x - 1)$ (Multiplication by 36)

$6x + 30 - 9x - 27 = 4x - 4$

$-7x = -7$

$x = 1$

(ii) $\dfrac{3a - 1}{3} + \dfrac{5}{12} - \dfrac{a}{4} = \dfrac{2a + 1}{5}$

$\dfrac{12a - 4 + 5 - 3a}{12} = \dfrac{2a + 1}{5}$ (Sometimes a simpler solution will result from grouping fractions with similar denominators)

$\dfrac{9a + 1}{12} = \dfrac{2a + 1}{5}$

$$45a + 5 = 24a + 12$$

$$21a = 7$$

$$a = \frac{1}{3}$$

Solution of linear equations in one variable involving literal coefficients.

The patterns that have been followed in solving equations in which the coefficients of the variables are arithmetic numbers are followed in solving equations having literal coefficients.

Sample solution:

Solve $s = \frac{n}{2}(a + l)$ for a

$$s = \frac{n}{2}(a + l)$$

$$s = \frac{n}{2}a + \frac{nl}{2}$$

$$2s = na + nl$$

$$na = 2s - nl$$

$$a = \frac{2s - nl}{n}$$

Study of the number of possible solutions of $ax + b = 0$

Conditions	$ax + b = 0$	x	Comments
$a, b \neq 0$	$ax + b = 0$	$-\dfrac{b}{a}$	one solution
$a \neq 0, b = 0$	$ax + 0 = 0$	0	one solution
$a = 0, b \neq 0$	$0(x) + b = 0$	unde-fined	no real solution
$a = b = 0$	$0(x) + 0 = 0$	$\dfrac{0}{0}$	indeterminate, any member of R may replace x.

2. Review of the rectangular Cartesian co-ordinate system, with practice in graphing ordered number pairs.

The Cartesian system of rectangular co-ordinates is based on (i) two real-number lines intersecting orthogonally with the zero points coincident, (ii) a one-to-one correspondence between sets of *ordered* pairs of numbers and points in the plane.

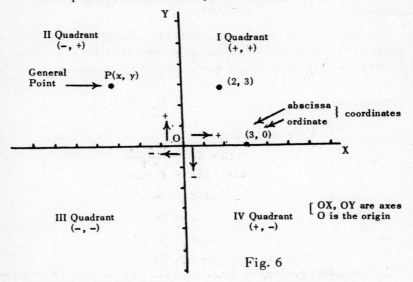

Fig. 6

Review of the solution of linear equations in two variables, stressing the use and graphical implications of equivalent systems of equations, and including examples with literal coefficients and a discussion of the possible number of roots.

Sample Solutions:

(a) Solve the equations $5x + y = 15$ and $2x - 3y = 6$ by elimination, substitution and comparison.

Elimination

$$5x + y = 15 \quad (1)$$
$$2x - 3y = 6 \quad (2)$$
$$(1) \times 3 \quad 15x + 3y = 45 \quad (3)$$
$$2x - 3y = 6 \quad (2)$$

Substitution

$$5x + y = 15 \quad (1)$$
$$2x - 3y = 6 \quad (2)$$
$$\text{from } (1) \quad y = 15 - 5x \quad (6)$$
$$\text{in } (2) \quad 2x - 3(15 - 5x) = 6 \quad (7)$$

Add $17x = 51$ $2x - 45 + 15x = 6$

             $x = 3$ (4) $17x = 51$

from $2x - 3y = 6$ (2) $x = 3$

obtain $y = 0$ (5) $\therefore$ $y = 0$

The solution set is $\{(3,0)\}$ The solution set is $\{(3, 0)\}$

Comparison

$$5x + y = 15 \qquad (1)$$

$$2x - 3y = 6 \qquad (2)$$

from (1) $y = 15 - 5x$ (8)

from (2) $y = \dfrac{6 - 2x}{-3}$ (9)

Compare (8) and (9)

$$15 - 5x = \frac{6 - 2x}{-3}$$

$$-45x + 15x = 6 - 2x$$

$$17x = 51$$

$$x = 3$$

$$y = 0$$

The solution set is $\{(3, 0)\}$

By *equivalent systems* is meant systems of equations which have the same solutions. Referring to the numbers of the equations just solved, we may say that one set of equivalent systems is
$\{(\,(1), (2)\,), (\,(3), (2)\,), (\,(4), (2)\,), (\,(4), (5)\,)\}$

An examination of the following graphs will point up the increased simplicity of the above set of equations. These equations define, initially, two oblique lines, but finally two lines parallel to the axis (one being the x-axis in this case).

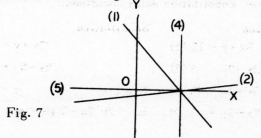

Fig. 7

22

(b) Illustrate the concept of equivalent systems of equations using $a_1 x + b_1 y = c$, and $a_2x + b_2y = c_2$. Discuss the possible number of solutions to these equations.

$$a_1x + b_1y = c_1 \qquad (1)$$

$$a_2x + b_2y = c_2 \qquad (2)$$

$(1) \times a_2 \qquad a_1a_2x + a_2b_1y = a_2c_1 \qquad (3)$

$(2) \times a_1 \qquad a_1a_2x + a_1b_2y = a_1c_2 \qquad (4)$

$(3) - (4) \qquad a_2b_1y - a_1b_2y = a_2c_1 - a_1c_2$

This is usually written in the form

$$(a_1b_2 - a_2b_1)y = a_1c_2 - a_2c_1$$

$$y = \frac{a_1c_2 - a_2c_1}{a_1b_2 + a_2b_1} \quad (a_1b_2 - a_2b_1 \neq 0)$$

In a similar manner, multiplying (1) by b_2 and (2) by b_1 and solving for x:

$$x = \frac{c_1b_2 - c_2b_1}{a_1b_2 - a_2b_1} \quad (a_1b_2 - a_2b_1 \neq 0)$$

Note:

The above solutions are frequently written in *determinant* form

as $x = \dfrac{\begin{vmatrix} c_1 & b_1 \\ c_2 & b_2 \end{vmatrix}}{\begin{vmatrix} a_1 & b_1 \\ a_2 & b_2 \end{vmatrix}}$ and $y = \dfrac{\begin{vmatrix} a_1 & c_1 \\ a_2 & c_2 \end{vmatrix}}{\begin{vmatrix} a_1 & b_1 \\ a_2 & b_2 \end{vmatrix}}$. The values, above, being

formed by multiplication and addition as shown by

or $c_1b_2 - c_2b_1$ which is the numerator for x.

It can be shown that either $a_1 x + b_1y = c_1$ or $a_2x + b_2y = c_2$ represents a straight line. It is also agreed that any two lines intersect in, at most, one point.

However, *three* cases arise here which are given special names:

consistent if the lines intersect, i.e. are not parallel hence
$a_1 : b_1 \neq a_2 : b_2$ or $a_1 : a_2 \neq b_1 : b_2$

inconsistent if the lines are parallel and therefore do not
intersect hence $a_1 : b_1 = a_2 : b_2$. Note here that
neither of these ratios may equal $c_1 : c_2$ which
would give rise to the final case.

linearly dependent if the lines coincide. This condition is
expressed as $a_1 : b_1 : c_1 = a_2 : b_2 : c_2$ which would
give rise to a common factor.
example: $3x + 4y = 12$ is the same line as
$9x + 12y = 36$. The above condition would mean that
$3 : 4 : -12 = 9 : 12 : -36$.

Cartesian product

For two sets $A = \{1, 2, 3, 4\}$, $B = \{7, 8, 9, 10\}$ the cartesian
produce $A \times B$, read "A cross B" refers to the set of ordered
pairs made up by each element from A being paired with each
element from B.

The cartesian product of A and B for the above sets would be

$(1, 7)$, $(1, 8)$, $(1, 9)$, $(1, 10)$

$(2, 7)$, $(2, 8)$, $(2, 9)$, $(2, 10)$

$(3, 7)$, $(3, 8)$, $(3, 9)$, $(3, 10)$

$(4, 7)$, $(4, 8)$, $(4, 9)$, $(4, 10)$

3. Binary relations

Binary relations imply an association of two objects. In
mathematics such relations usually contain connectives like
"is equal to," "is a member of," "is greater than."

The set of ordered pairs determined by a relation

Because a relation *is* a set of ordered pairs we usually think
of the set of ordered pairs determined by a *defining sentence*.
We say that the relation carries three requirements with it, viz.
a domain, a range, and a defining sentence.

The domain and range of a relation

The *domain* is the set of first elements of a relation.
The *range* is the set of second elements of a relation.

24

Some mathematicians feel that it is necessary to mention the *universe* for the domain and/or the range as being the set from which the elements of the domain and range are chosen.

Linear equality and inequality relations and their graphs.

A linear function is one defined by a polynominal of the first degree, e.g. $y = mx + b$. We read the notation $f : x \rightarrow mx + b$ as "the function that maps x into mx + b."

You should be able to do two main types of questions.

(a) Draw the graph of the function defined by $2x - 3y + 16 = 0$

Solution:

Table of values

$$x = \frac{3y + 16}{2}$$

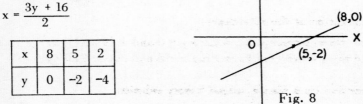

x	8	5	2
y	0	-2	-4

Fig. 8

(b) Find the equation which defines the linear function g that maps 3 into 4, and 8 into -3.

Solution:

The graph is a straight line
which passes through the points
A (3, 4) and B (8, -3).
The slope is $\dfrac{-3 - 4}{8 - 3} = \dfrac{-7}{5}$

The required equation is

$$y - 4 = \frac{-7}{5} (x - 3)$$

$$y = \frac{-7}{5} x + \frac{21}{4} + 4$$

$$y = \frac{-7}{5} x + 9\frac{1}{4}$$

$$\therefore g : x \longrightarrow \frac{-7}{5} x + 9\frac{1}{4}$$

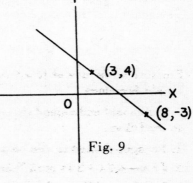

Fig. 9

To plot inequalities first plot a boundary defined by an equation, then determine the exact location of the region with reference to the boundary.

Sample solution:

Plot the graph of the inequation.
x + y > 2

Solution:

Plot the graph of points defined by x + y = 2 using a dotted line. Shade in the region as shown in fig. 10

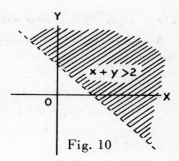

Fig. 10

Determination of the intercepts

Find the x-intercept by setting y = 0 and solving for x.
Find the y-intercept by setting x = 0 and solving for y.

4. Function as a single valued binary relation

In words, a function is single valued if no two first-elements of its ordered pairs are the same.

Graphically:

Any line drawn parallel to the y-axis will cut the graph *once only.*

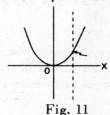

Fig. 11

Practice in the use of functional notation. Graphical study of simple functions.

You should understand the notations listed here, and know how to read them.

1. f a symbol used to denote a function.
2. f : x ⟶ 2x + 3 is read "the function which maps x into 2x + 3".
3. f(x) is read "f at x" or "f of x". It is the ordinate of the of the ordered pair (x, f (x)).

Examples of binary relations that are not functions

In general, any set of ordered pairs in which two or more first elements are the same, is not a function, but is a relation.

These mappings illustrate the difference between relation and function.

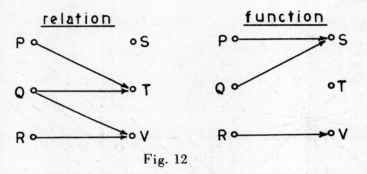

Fig. 12

5. **Examples of linear functions developed from problems in which the domain is the natural numbers, the integers, or the reals.**

6. **The linear equation of the form y = mx + b.**
   The role of each of the parameters m and b.
   The general linear equation ax + by + c = 0

Any graphs you have drawn which result in straight lines have been defined by equations which have, at most, an x-term, a y-term and a constant (or absolute) term.

In general this means that the equation ax + by + c = 0 defines a straight line. You have taken no proof of this up to now. A convenient method of writing the defining sentence for a line is y = mx + b. (1)

If we reduce the equation ax + by + c = 0 to the above form we obtain

$$ax + by + c = 0$$

$$\therefore \quad -by = ax + c$$

$$y = -\frac{a}{b}x - \frac{c}{b}$$

In equation (1) m is the slope, and b is the y-intercept.
In terms of ax + by + c = 0 we say slope $= -\dfrac{a}{b}$
y-intercept $= -\dfrac{c}{b}$.

Line-patterns or *families* obtained by varying m or b in the
equation y = mx + b.

Keep b fixed and vary m   Keep m fixed and vary b

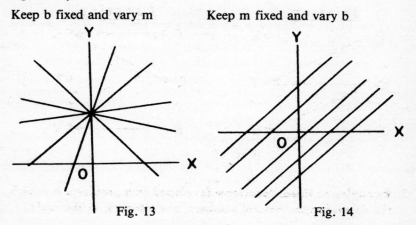

Fig. 13   Fig. 14

**Review of the point-slope form, the slope y-intercept form, and
the slope x-intercept form.**
Reduction of ax + by + c = 0 to the slope y-intercept form.

point-slope form $\qquad y - y_1 = m(x - x_1)$

slope y-intercept form $\qquad y = mx + b$

slope x-intercept form $\qquad y = m(x - a)$

The reduction of the equation ax + by + c = 0 is shown in the
previous section. Note the values for slope and y-intercept. Some
mathematicians use these as formulas.

UNIT 2: THE EXPONENTIAL AND LOGARITHMIC FUNCTIONS (5 TO 6 WEEKS)

This unit introduces a study of the graphs of the exponential
and logarithmic functions, and develops the mathematical basis
for the use of logarithmic. Some practice in the use of logarithmic for computation is included, but the stress in on the
mathematical interpretations.

1. Review of the concept of power, base, exponent (or index)

The definition of a^x where x is a positive integer, and a is a real number.

The notation a^x denotes a *power* in which x is the *exponent* and a is the *base*. Where x is a positive integer, and a is a real number, a^x means x factors of a.

The development of and practice with the laws of exponents where x is a positive integer.

In the following equations $x \in {}^+I$ and $a \in R$ for the power of the form a^x.

1. $(a^m)(a^n) = a^{m+n}$

2. $a^m \div a^n = a^{m-n} \ (m>n)$

$$= 1 \qquad (m=n)$$

$$= \frac{1}{a^{n-m}} \ (n>m)$$

3. $(a^m)^n = a^{mn}$

4. $(a^m)(b^m) = (ab)^m$

5. $a^m \div b^m = (\frac{a}{b})^m$

Note: that $a^0 = 1$ by a definition which keeps the system consistent.

2. Assumption of the laws for exponents where the base is ᵻ positive and the exponent is rational.

Interpretation fo a^x where x is rational and a is positive, and a demonstration of the need for restricting the nature of the base.

Practice with the laws for rational exponents and positive bases.

The first part of this heading means that, in order to keep the system of mathematics consistent, we have placed limitations on the values that a may take when $x \in Q$. The limitation is that $a > 0$.

Note also that although we define $\sqrt{a} \ \sqrt{b} = \sqrt{ab}$ for the product of two radicals, the definition does not hold for

$\sqrt{-a}$ $\sqrt{-b}$ (a, b > 0) which may also be written
$\sqrt{-1}$ $\sqrt{a}$ $\sqrt{-1}$ $\sqrt{b}$ or $\sqrt{-1}$ $\sqrt{-1}$ $\sqrt{a}$ $\sqrt{b}$ by the associative
property for addition. Because $\sqrt{-1}$ cannot be found in the real
number system we invent a number whose square is -1, namely
$i^2 = -1$. Hence $\sqrt{-1}$ $\sqrt{-1}$ $\sqrt{a}$ $\sqrt{b}$ = $i^2\sqrt{ab}$ = $-\sqrt{ab}$

You should be able to operate on rational and irrational
exponents using the same laws as those indicated at the
beginning of Unit 2.

Examples: (In this section all variables are positive real numbers)

1. $(10\ a^{1/2}\ b^{2/3})\ (3\ a^2 b)$

   $= 30\ a^{5/2}\ b^{5/3}$

2. $(\sqrt{3}\ a^{3/2}\ b^{5/4}) \div (a^{1/2}\ b^{3/4})$

   $= \sqrt{3}\ a b^{1/2}$

3. $(q^{-4/3})^3$

   $= q^{-4}$

4. $a^{2/3}\ b^{2/3}$

   $= (a\ b)^{2/3}$

5. $a^{1/2} \div b^{1/2}$

   $= (\frac{a}{b})^{1/2}$

Scientific notation

**Practice in multiplication and division involving the use of
scientific (or standard) notation.**

In scientific (standard) notation, any number which is recorded
is written with a decimal following the first non - zero digit, and
an appropriate power of 10 used as a factor. Thus 245, in scientific notation, would be written 2.45×10^2.

ntific notation serves three purposes:

(i) It is a convenient way to write very large numbers.

e.g. $186,000 = 1.86 \times 10^5$

(ii) It is a convenient way to write very small numbers.

e.g. $.0000496 = 4.96 \times 10^{-5}$

(iii) The first factor of the number in scientific notation records all the significant digits in an approximate number.

e.g. In (i), above, the number 186,000 represents the speed of light in miles per second. As this number is only accurate to three figures it is written as 1.86×10^5 in scientific notation.

You should be able to multiply and divide using standard notation.

Examples:

1. 5000×0.00013

$= 5.0 \times 10^3 \times 1.3 \times 10^{-4}$

$= 5.0 \times 1.3 \times 10^3 \times 10^{-4}$

$= 6.5 \times 10^{-1}$

$= 0.65$

2. $1.20 \times 10^{-3} \div (4.0 \times 10^5)$

$= 1.20 \div 4.0 \times (10^{-3} \div 10^5)$

$= 0.30 \times 10^{-8}$

$= 3.0 \times 10^{-9}$

$= 0.000000003$

3. Assumption of the laws for exponents where the base is positive and the exponent is real.

Drawing the graphs of the exponential function defined by the equations $y = 2^x$, $y = 3^x$, $y = 10^x$.

Study of these graphs to illustrate the rate of exponential growth.

The first part of this heading means that, in order to keep the system of mathematics consistent, we have placed limitations on the values that a may take when $x \in R$. The limitation is that $a > 0$.

Any standard text book containing a section on exponential functions will include carefully drawn graphs of these functions. However, *you should draw at least one* if you are to understand the function fully.

Table of Values $(y = 2^x)$

x	-1	0	1	2	3	4	5	6
y	½	1	2	4	8	16	32	64

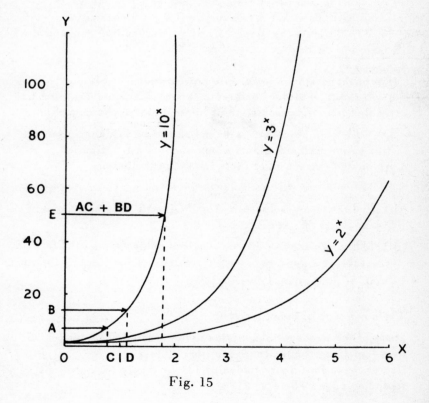

Fig. 15

A study of the curves in figure 15 will show the following ideas, among others:

(a) As x increases, y increases. The function is called an *increasing function*.

(b) For x = 2, the value of y = 10^x is 100
the value of y = 3^x is 9
the value of y = 2^x is 4.

A similar examination for x = 3 and x = 4 will show that 10^x *grows* much faster than 3^x or 2^x.

(c) An examination of Δy (the change in y) for equal Δx in each case will show that Δy is greater for y = 10^x than for y = 3^x or y = 2^x. Thus the slope $\dfrac{\Delta y}{\Delta x}$ of the curves increases as the base increases.

Use of these graphs for simple computations involving multiplication, division, and roots, where the exponents must be estimated from the graph (Use of large scale graphs suggested.)

The following procedure is based on the lettering arrangement in fig. 15 for performing operations such as multiplication, division and extraction of roots by use of the graph.

(i) Two numbers will normally be given on which to operate.

(ii) Find these as ordinates OA and OB with the corresponding abscissas AC and BD.

(iii) Add, subtract or divide as required using AC and BD to establish a new abscissa (AC + BD is shown on the diagram)

(iv) OE is the estimated "answer".

The advantage of using base 10

Study of the exponential function using ordered pairs for y = 10^x from four-figure tables (antilogarithm tables)
Use of these four-figure tables of 10^x in simple computations, including cases where x > 1.

The advantages of base 10 over other bases:

(a) Because the graph of ordered pairs defined by y = 10^x grows more rapidly than that defined by y = 2^x we may do more calculations graphically on a reasonable size of graph.

(b) In many cases the calculations are simpler because the exponents are smaller.

(c) Because our number system is a decimal one, numbers of any size are readily reduced to standard form using 10 with a convenient exponent as a factor.

In calculating using logarithms to base 10 we find that the logarithm is made up of two parts, a *characteristic* and a *mantissa*, e.g. because $6.266 = 10^{0.937}$ we say log $6.266 = 0.937$

because $\quad 62.66 = 10^{1.937}$ we say log $\quad 62.66 = 1.937$

because $\quad 8.650 = 10^{0.797}$ we say log $\quad 8.650 = 0.797$

because $0.01629 = 10^{\bar{2}.212}$ we say log $0.01629 = \bar{2}.212$

The *characteristics* are integers which precede the decimal point.

The *mantissas* are decimal fractions, always positive, which follow the decimal point.

To find the characteristic write the number in scientific notation. The exponent of the factor of 10 in this form is the characteristic, e.g. $62.66 = 6.266 \times 10^1$ therefore the characteristic of log 62.66 is 1.

To find the mantissa look up any set of logarithm tables.

The key to accurate calculation is method. Write the "logarithm program" carefully and neatly. It will help you to check your work if any error has occurred.

Example: Evaluate $\dfrac{37.7 \times 0.0023 \times 0.0517}{49.6 \times 0.00514}$

Solution:

let x $= \dfrac{37.7 \times 0.0023 \times 0.0517}{49.6 \times 0.00514}$

log 37.7	= 1.5763	log 49.6	= 1.6955
log 0.0023	= $\bar{3}$.3617	log 0.00514	= $\bar{3}$.7110
log 0.0517	= $\bar{2}$.7135		$\bar{1}$.4065
	$\bar{3}$.6515		
	$\bar{1}$.4065 ← Subtract		
	$\bar{2}$.2450		

34

x = antilog $\overline{2}$.2450
 = 0.01758
 = 0.0176 correct to three figures.

4. Study and comparison of the graphs of y = 10ˣ and x = 10ʸ

Study of the set of ordered pairs (x, y) satisfying x = 10ʸ where x is such that
  (i) y may be determined by inspection
  (ii) logarithm tables are necessary to determine y

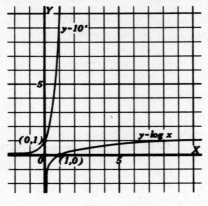

Fig. 16

The two curves shown in fig. 16 are graphs of *inverse functions*. The inverse of a function is determined by reversing the ordered pair, and the domain and range. A function and its inverse have the line defined by y = x as axis of symmetry.

The graph of the function defined by y = 10ˣ is called an exponential curve.

The graph of the function defined by x = 10ʸ is called a logarithmic curve.

The study of the logarithmic curve gives rise to the notation y = $\log_{10}$x in which the ordinate of any point on the curve is the exponent of the power of 10 which equals the abscissa.

In the graph, fig. 16, some values of y may be obtained from the curve, viz. values for x = 1 and x = 10 where the values of y are 0 and 1 respectively.

Intermediate points have ordinates whose values should be found from tables. For example log 2 = .3010, and log 5 = 0.6990. You should check these against the graph, fig. 16, for comparison.

Use of the notation $y = \log_{10} x$

Development of the basic properties of logarithms.

Practice in computations involving the use of logarithms for products, quotients, powers, and roots using four-place tables. (Computation of roots stressed)

Because logarithms are exponents (or indices) the laws governing exponents, and those governing logarithms *should be* the same.

Name of operation	by exponents	by logarithms
multiplication	addition	addition?
division	subtraction	subtraction?
powers	multiplication	multiplication?
roots	division	division?

Because we would like the question marks to be eliminated in the above table we write down, in logarithmic notation, the properties that should follow from a consideration of the exponent properties,

viz.   (1) $\log_a MN = \log_a M + \log_a N$

(2) $\log_a \dfrac{M}{N} = \log_a M - \log_a N$

(3) $\log_a M^p = p \log_a M$

(4) $\log_a \sqrt[q]{M} = \dfrac{1}{q} \log_a M$

With suitable restrictions on M, N, and a, the proofs of these basic properties are listed in any standard mathematics text written for this grade level.

Sample Calculations: (Various methods of recording solutions may be used)

1. Evaluate $\sqrt[3]{56.4}$

   Solution: let $x = (56.4)^{\frac{1}{3}}$

   then $\log x = \frac{1}{3} \log 56.4$

   $$\left[\begin{array}{l} \log 56.4 = 1.7513 \\ \qquad 3\overline{)1.7513} \\ \qquad\qquad .5838 \end{array}\right.$$

   $$= .5838$$

   $$x = 3.84$$

2. Evaluate $\sqrt[5]{0.03285}$

   Solution: let $x = (0.03285)^{\frac{1}{5}}$

   $$\left[\begin{array}{l} \log 0.03285 = \bar{2}.5166 \\ \qquad 5\overline{)\,\bar{2}.5166} \\ \qquad 5\overline{)\,\bar{5} + 3.5166} \\ \tfrac{1}{5} \log 0.03285 = \bar{1}.7013 \end{array}\right.$$

   $$x = 0.5027$$

5. Discussion of simple and compound interest

Development of the formula for simple interest $A = P(1 + ni)$

Development of the formula for compound interest $A = P(1 + i)^n$

In these formulas A is the *amount*, or present value; the sum of the quantity of money invested (the principal, P) and the interest earned, I. The symbol, n, represents the number of interest periods (usually one year unless otherwise stated).

The development of the formula is an *inductive* one in most texts (look up the meaning of the word *inductive* in the list of definitions).

People frequently invest money in order to obtain an income from it. If they collect the interest each period, and use it (say, to live on) then this interest is said to be simple interest. The principal remains a fixed amount.

Sometimes money is invested, and the interest earned is added to the principal and re-invested. Such interest is said to be *compounded*, i.e. the principal increases as each interest period is reached.

Practice with numerical examples involving simple and compound interest.

Because these are the first of a number of *formulas* that you may have to fill in during this study, a few comments are in order.

(i) Formulas can become the handy tool which will produce answers *without understanding*.

(ii) Note that *understanding* is one of the main aims of the new approach in mathematics.

(iii) Any diagram, comment, or statement which you care to write down in the course of solving problems, which may be done by formulas, will help your understanding of a good solution.

Example 1:

Find, to the nearest dollar, the amount of $600. at simple interest at 6% for a term of 4 years.

Solution:

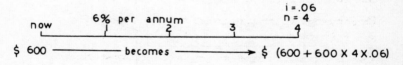

Fig. 17

From the diagram, $A = 600 + 600 \times 4 \times .06$,

$$= 600 + 144,$$

$$= 744$$

∴ the amount is $744.

Example 2:

Find the accumulated value to the nearest dollar, at compound interest, of $250. in 6 years at 4% (compounded annually).

38

Solution:

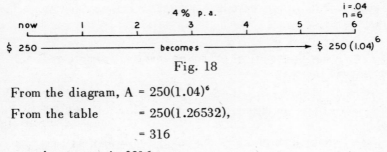

Fig. 18

From the diagram, $A = 250(1.04)^6$

From the table $= 250(1.26532),$

$= 316$

∴ the amount is $316.

Study of the graphs of the functions defined by these relations.

Examination of the formulas $A = P(1 + ni)$ and $A = P(1 + i)^n$ will show that the first defines a linear relation while the second defines an exponential relationship. Here is a diagram showing the difference, graphically. Where the ordinate at any point on each line (curved or straight) is the amount at any given time, it is obvious that the compounding of interest increases the *rate of growth* of a given sum of money.

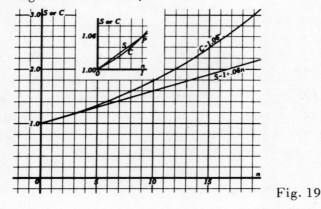

Fig. 19

Calculations of equivalent annual rate in cases where the compounding is semi-annual, quarterly, monthly.

Example:

Find the annual rate equivalent to a rate of 1.5% compounded monthly.

Solution:

Calculations

In 1 year, $1 at 1.5% monthly, will amount to $1(1.015)^{12}$

In 1 year, $1 at rate i compounded annually, will amount to $(1 + i)$

$\left.\right\}$ Find the two amounts, one in the monthly and one in the annual compounding

$1 + i = (1.015)^{12}$

$\left.\right\}$ Because these are the *same amounts*, set them equal.

From tables $i = 1.19562 - 1$,

$= 0.19562$

$\left.\right\}$ Solve for i.

∴ the equivalent annual rate is 19.6%.

Note: — As a check it is convenient to see that the equivalent annual rate is greater than a direct multiplication would indicate (say $1.5 \times 12 = 18$!)

Calculation of Principal

By dividing each side of the equation $A = P(1 + ni)$ by the coefficient of P we find

$$P = \frac{A}{1 + ni} \qquad (1)$$

By dividing each side of the equation $A = P(1 + i)^n$ by the coefficient of P we find

$$P = \frac{A}{(1 + i)^n} \qquad (2)$$

6. Supplementary

The mathematical theory of the slide rule as applied to multiplication, division and square roots.

UNIT 3: QUADRATIC FUNCTIONS AND QUADRATIC EQUATIONS (6 WEEKS)

1. Simple quadratic functions and their graphs to include general form, symmetry, domain, range, intercepts, type of opening, the

existence of a maximum or minimum value, the regions defined by the associated inequalities.

A quadratic function is a set of ordered pairs defined by an equation in which the highest power of the variable is the second. Thus, $y = x^2$, $y = x^2 + 2x + 3$, $y = kx^2$ would each define a quadratic function.

One of the key features in discussing the quadratic function and/or its defining sentence is that x^2 is always positive, regardless of the value of x, and has a minimum value of 0. In fact, the square of *any* real number is positive.

(1) $y = 2x^2$

x	−4	−3	−2	−1	0	+1	+2	+3	+4
$2x^2$	+32	+18	+8	+2	0	+2	+8	+18	+32

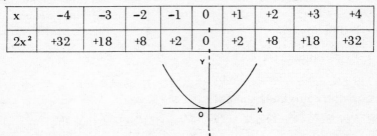

(2) $y = 2(x + 2)^2$ or $y = 2x^2 + 8x + 8$

x	−6	−5	−4	−3	−2	−1	0	+1	+2
$2(x + 2)^2$	32	18	8	2	0	2	8	18	32

(3) $y = 2(x + 2)^2 + 4$ or $y = 2x^2 + 8x + 12$

x	−6	−5	−4	−3	−2	−1	0	+1	+2
$2(x + 2)^2 + 4$	36	22	12	6	4	6	12	22	36

Fig. 20

Some discussion points on examination of fig. 20.

(1) All these "quadratic curves" are similar in shape. Their upward opening, coupled with the fact that all squares are positive, leads to the conjecture that, if the coefficient of x^2 or of $(x + 2)^2$ were negative, the curve would open downward. This, in fact, is the case.

(2) In (2) of fig. 20, when $x + 2 = 0$, i.e. $x = -2$ (i) a minimum is is reached; (ii) an axis of symmetry is found to be defined by $x + 2 = 0$ and (iii) the coordinates of the minimum point are $(-2, 0)$.

(3) In (3) of fig. 20, the defining sentence shifts the origin to the right and down i.e. the *vertex* of the parabola is shifted to the left and up. The coordinates of the vertex are $(-2, 4)$. Note the change, or lack of change, in the signs of 2 and 4 from the defining sentence.

(4) The form of the defining sentences in (2) and (3) results from a procedure called "completing the square", performed on the defining sentences $y = 2x^2 + 8x + 8$ and $y = 2x^2 + 8x + 12$. In the completed square form you should see some relationships which exist between the various coefficients and terms of the defining sentence and (i) the opening, (ii) the axis of symmetry, and (iii) the coordinates of the vertex in the graph of the function.

Note: The general quadratic equation is $y = ax^2 + bx + c$

The inequalities associated with $y = 2x^2$ are $y > 2x^2$, $y < 2x^2$, $y \geq 2x^2$, $y \leq 2x^2$. As in the case of linear inequalities, once the boundary has been established, the region defined is determined by the direction of the inequality sign and the direction of opening of the curve. The convention with regard to solid or dotted lines still holds.

2. The quadratic equation and its graphical solution:

Example:
Find the x-intercepts of the curve defined by $y = 2x^2 + 2x - 12$

Solution:
The x-intercepts are found by setting $y = 0$ in the defining sentence.

i.e. $2x^2 + 2x - 12 = 0$

$x^2 + x - 6 = 0$

$(x + 3)(x - 2) = 0$

$x = -3$ or $x = 2$

∴ the x-intercepts are –3 and +2.

Some writers may ask the above question in other ways. Here are some of them.

(i) Find the values of x for which the ordinates of the ordered pairs are zero in the defining sentence $y = 2x^2 + 2x - 12$

(ii) Find the "zeros" of the equation $y = 2x^2 + 2x - 12$

(iii) Solve the equation $2x^2 + 2x - 12 = 0$.

However, *all* the above questions require as a solution the values of the first member of an ordered pair (or ordered pairs) whose second member(s) is/are zero.

Some mathematicians draw a dotted parabola in these cases, indicating that the points where the graph cuts the x-axis form the complete required graph.

3. Review of the factoring of quadratic polynomials

You should be familiar with the following methods:

(a) Remove the common factor.

$ax + bx = x(a + b)$

(b) The difference of squares.

$a^2 - b^2 = (a + b)(a - b)$

(c) Grouping to obtain a common factor.

$ab + ac + db + dc = a(b + c) + d(b + c)$
$$= (b + c)(a + d)$$

(d) Grouping to obtain the difference of squares.

$a^2 - b^2 + 2bc - c^2 = a^2 - (b^2 - 2bc + c^2)$
$$= a^2 - (b - c)^2$$
$$= [a - (b - c)][a + (b - c)]$$
$$= (a - b + c)(a + b - c)$$

(e) The trinomial.

    (i) Inspection

       $x^2 + 5x + 4 = (x + 4)(x + 1)$

(ii) Complete square
$$9a^2 - 24ab + 16b^2 = (3a - 4b)^2$$

(iii) Decomposition of the centre term
$$15a^2 - 17ab + 4b^2$$
> Find two numbers whose sume is −17 and
> whose product is $15 \times 4 = 60$
> the numbers are −12 and −5
$$= 15a^2 - 12ab - 5ab + 4b^2$$
$$= 3a(5a - 4b) - b(5a - 4b)$$
$$= (5a - 4b)(3a - b)$$

(iv) Completion of the square
$$2x^2 - 10x + 12$$
$$= 2(x^2 - 5x + {}^{12}\!/\!_2)$$
$$= 2(x^2 - 5x + {}^{25}\!/\!_4 + {}^{12}\!/\!_2 - {}^{25}\!/\!_4)$$
$$= 2[(x - {}^5\!/\!_2)^2 - {}^1\!/\!_4]$$
$$= 2(x - {}^5\!/\!_2 + {}^1\!/\!_2)(x - {}^5\!/\!_2 - {}^1\!/\!_2)$$
$$= 2(x - 2)(x - 3)$$

(f) The factor theorem
let $f = x^2 - 4$
$\because$ $f(2) = 0$
$\therefore$ x − 2 is a factor of f.
$\because$ $f(-2) = 0$
$\therefore$ x + 2 is a factor of f

Thus the factors are x − 2 and x + 2.

Although the course of study implies that these factoring methods should be learned for quadratic polynomials it should be noted that *this* method is preferred for many polynomials of higher order than the second.

(g) The formula
$$ax^2 + bx + c = (x - \frac{-b + \sqrt{b^2 - 4ac}}{2a})(x - \frac{-b - \sqrt{b^2 - 4ac}}{2a})$$

Algebraic solutions of quadratic equations by factoring and by completing the square.

Finding maximum and minimum values of quadratic functions by completing the square.

44

Example 1:
Find the maximum (or minimum) value for the function defined by $y = 4x^2 + x - 6$.

Solution:
$y = 4x^2 + x - 6$ represents a parabola which opens upward and has a minimum value

$$y = 4x^2 + x - 6$$
$$= 4(x^2 + \tfrac{1}{4}x) - 6$$
$$= 4(x^2 + \tfrac{1}{4}x + \tfrac{1}{64}) - 6 - \tfrac{1}{16}$$
$$= 4(x + \tfrac{1}{8})^2 - \tfrac{97}{16}$$

The minimum value of the function is $-\tfrac{97}{16}$

Example 2:
Find the maximum (or minimum) value for the function defined by $y = -6x^2 + 3x - 2$.

Solution:
$y = -6x^2 + 3x - 2$ represents a parabola which opens downward and has a maximum value

$$y = -6x^2 + 3x - 2$$
$$= -6(x^2 - \tfrac{1}{2}x) - 2$$
$$= -6(x^2 - \tfrac{1}{2}x + \tfrac{1}{16}) - 2 + \tfrac{3}{8}$$
$$= -6(x - \tfrac{1}{4})^2 - \tfrac{13}{8}$$

The maximum value of the function is $-\tfrac{13}{8}$

4. The general quadratic equation $ax^2 + bx + c = 0$ and the development of its roots $\dfrac{-b + \sqrt{b^2 - 4ac}}{2a}$ and $\dfrac{-b - \sqrt{b^2 - 4ac}}{2a}$

Discussion of the case of non-real roots

Recognition of the need of an extension of the number system beyond the reals.

Solution		*Method*
$ax^2 + bx + c = 0$		
$ax^2 + bx = -c$	. . . . .	1. Move the absolute term to the right hand side.
$x^2 + \dfrac{b}{a}x = -\dfrac{c}{a}$	. . . . .	2. Divide each side by the coefficient of x^2.

$$x^2 + \frac{b}{a}x + \frac{b^2}{4a^2} = \frac{b^2}{4a^2} - \frac{c}{a} \quad \cdots$$

3. Add the square of half the new coefficient of x to each side (i.e. complete the square on the left hand side.)

$$(x + \frac{b}{2a})^2 = \frac{b^2 - 4ac}{4ac} \quad \cdots$$

4. Factor the left hand side and simplify the right side.

$$x + \frac{b}{2a} = \frac{\pm\sqrt{b^2 - 4ac}}{2a} \quad \cdots$$

5. Take the square root of each side.

$$x = \frac{-b \pm \sqrt{b^2 - 4ac}}{2a}$$

6. Solve for x.

Hence the roots of the general quadratic equation are
$$\frac{-b + \sqrt{b^2 - 4ac}}{2a} \text{ and } \frac{-b - \sqrt{b^2 - 4ac}}{2a}$$

Example 1:
Solve $2x^2 - 7x + 4 = 0$

Solution I:
Solve by completion of the square. (Compare this with the method outlined above.)

$$2x^2 - 7x + 4 = 0$$
$$2x^2 - 7x = -4$$
$$x^2 - \tfrac{7}{2}x = -2$$
$$x^2 - \tfrac{7}{2}x + \tfrac{49}{16} = -2 + \tfrac{49}{16}$$
$$(x - \tfrac{7}{4})^2 = \tfrac{17}{16}$$
$$x - \tfrac{7}{4} = \frac{\pm\sqrt{17}}{4}$$
$$x = \frac{7 \pm \sqrt{17}}{4}$$

∴ the roots of the equation are $\dfrac{7 + \sqrt{17}}{4}$ and $\dfrac{7 - \sqrt{17}}{4}$

Solution II:
Solve by means of the formula.
$$2x^2 - 7x + 4 = 0$$

In this quadratic equation, comparison with the general equation suggests that we use the substitutions a = 2, b = -7, c = 4.

46

Then the roots are $\dfrac{-b + \sqrt{b^2 - 4ac}}{2a} = \dfrac{7 + \sqrt{49 - 32}}{4} = \dfrac{7 + \sqrt{17}}{4}$

and $\dfrac{-b - \sqrt{b^2 - 4ac}}{2a} = \dfrac{7 - \sqrt{49 - 32}}{4} = \dfrac{7 - \sqrt{17}}{4}$

These correspond with the roots found in Solution I.

Example 2:
   Solve $3x^2 - 3x + 1 = 0$

Solution:
   Set $a = 3$, $b = -3$, $c = 1$

Then the roots are $\dfrac{3 + \sqrt{9 - 12}}{6} = \dfrac{3 + \sqrt{-3}}{6}$

and $\dfrac{3 - \sqrt{9 - 12}}{6} = \dfrac{3 + \sqrt{-3}}{6}$

Here is the first mention (in this course) of the square root of a negative number. According to this, we should find a number whose square is –3. Our study has shown that the square of any *real* number is positive. *There appears to be a need for a new set of numbers, whose squares are negative.*

We *invent* a number $i^2 = -1$, and agree that $i = \pm\sqrt{-1}$. Frequently we say $i = \sqrt{-1}$, using the principal root. (see p. 29)

Study of the form of the *complex* roots lead to the conjecture that if a and b are any real numbers, then $a + bi$ is the most complicated number we have come across to date.

$a + bi$ is a *complex unreal number*

a is a *real number*

bi is a *pure imaginary*.

5. Word problems giving rise to quadratic equations (inadmissable solutions treated by *prior* consideration of the domain.)

The problem of estimating answers as a rough check of the sense of the solution you have found is one which has been used for some time by good mathematicians.

However, for some time, we have persisted in obtaining several answers to a problem, and discarding the ones that did not suit the problem. We now use the method of *pre-examination* of the problem to determine the range of values available. We then choose the solution from this range.

Example:

If a car travelled 10 miles per hour faster, it would require 2 hours less time to travel 315 miles. What is the car's present speed?

Solution:

Let the present speed be x (where $x \in {}^+R$)

	Speed	Distance	Time
now	x	315	$\dfrac{315}{x}$
then	x + 10	315	$\dfrac{315}{x + 10}$

$$\frac{315}{x} = \frac{315}{x + 10} + 2$$

$2x^2 + 20x - 3150 = 0$

$x^2 + 10x - 1575 = 0$

$(x + 45)(x - 35) = 0$

$x = -45$ or $x = 35$

∴ the present speed is 35.

Note: The value −45 is automatically discarded because it does not belong to ^+R.

6. An inductive development of the factor theorem

Equations of degree higher than the second which may be solved by factoring.

If $P(x) = x^4 + 2x^3 + x + 2$

$\qquad = (x + 1)(x + 2)(x^2 - x + 1)$ in factored form,

then the values of x which make $P(x) = 0$ are those that make one of the factors equal to zero, viz. $x = -1$, $x = -2$ (there is no real value of x which will make $x^2 - x + 1 = 0$).

The above illustration suggests that, in general, if *a* replacing x in $P(x)$ makes $P(x) = 0$ then $x - a$ is a factor of $P(x)$.

Further examination of the formation of terms in the polynomial will show that the final term is the product of the last terms in the factors (one "last term" being chosen from each factor). This limits the number of trials we must make in factoring by means of the Factor Theorem. For example, in the polynomial $x^4 + 2x^3 + x + 2$, because the last term has factors ± 1, ± 2 it would be fruitless to suppose that $P(x)$ would be zero for any values of x other than these four.

The Factor Theorem may be used as an *initial* step in factoring expressions of degree greater than two.

Example 1:
Factor $p^3 - 6p^2 - 9p + 14$

Solution:
Let $f(p) = p^3 - 6p^2 - 9p + 14$
(1) Use factors of $+14$ to test, viz, ± 1, ± 2, ± 7, ± 14.
$\therefore f(1) = 0 \qquad \therefore p - 1$ is a factor.
(2) Find a second factor by division.
$f = (p - 1)(p^2 - 5p - 14)$
(3) Factor the trinomial as $(p - 7)(p + 2)$
thus $f = (p - 1)(p - 7)\ (p + 2)$ in factor form.

After the use of the factor theorem many of the "standard arrangements" for factoring will work.

Equations involving radical signs which give rise to quadratic equations in one variable.

Equations where the variable is other than x, eg.,
$$6 \sin^2\theta + \sin\theta - 2 = 0$$
$$2^{2x} - 12(2^x) + 32 = 0$$

Example 1:
Solve $\sqrt{p} - 3 = p - 5$

Solution:
$\sqrt{p} - 3 = p - 5 \qquad (1)$

Square $p - 3 = p^2 - 10p + 25 \qquad (2)$

$p^2 - 11p + 28 = 0 \qquad (3)$
$(p - 4)(p - 7) = 0$
If there are roots to the given equation they are 4 or 7.

Check (1)
If p = 4
L.S. = $\sqrt{1}$ = 1
R.S. = 4 - 5 = -1
∴ 4 is not a root.

(2)
If p = 7
L.S. = $\sqrt{4}$ = 2
R.S. = 7 - 5 = 2
∴ 7 is the correct root.

Note that step (2) of the solution is not reversible. It is at this stage that extraneous roots enter the solution.

Example 2:
Solve $6 \sin^2\theta + \sin\theta - 2 = 0$ for $\sin\theta$

Solution:
In patterns such as this it is usual to think of the quadratic equation $6x^2 + x - 2 = 0$. When x is known, then the value(s) of $\sin\theta$ are known.

Example 3:
Solve $2^{2x} - 12(2^x) + 32 = 0$

Solution:
Rewrite the given equation as $(2^x)^2 - 12(2^x) + 32 = 0$ and solve for 2^x. Then solve for x by taking the logarithm of each side if necessary.

7. Graphical study of the quadratic function for the cases where the roots of the corresponding equation are real and equal, real and unequal, and non-real.

The discriminant of a quadratic equation and its use in determining the character of the roots.

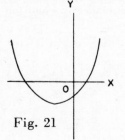

Fig. 21

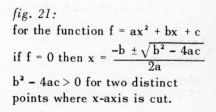

fig. 21:
for the function $f = ax^2 + bx + c$

if $f = 0$ then $x = \dfrac{-b \pm \sqrt{b^2 - 4ac}}{2a}$

$b^2 - 4ac > 0$ for two distinct points where x-axis is cut.

50

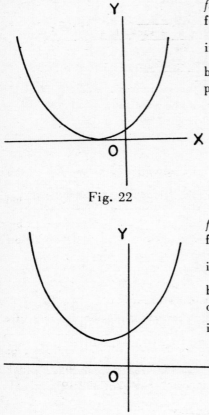

fig 22:
for the function f = ax² + bx + c

if f = 0 then x = $\dfrac{-b \pm \sqrt{b^2 - 4ac}}{2a}$

b² − 4ac = 0 for two identical
points where x-axis is cut.

Fig. 22

fig 23:
for the function f = ax² + bx + c

if f = 0 then x = $\dfrac{-b \pm \sqrt{b^2 - 4ac}}{2a}$

b² − 4ac < 0 for no real points
of intersection with the x-axis.

i.e. $\sqrt{b^2 - 4ac}$ is unreal.

Fig. 23

The sum and product of the roots of a quadratic equation and their use as a check on the roots

The formation of a quadratic equation when given its roots.

The roots of the general quadratic equation are:

$\dfrac{-b + \sqrt{b^2 - 4ac}}{2a}$ and $\dfrac{-b - \sqrt{b^2 - 4ac}}{2a}$

Sum of the roots is $\dfrac{-b + \sqrt{b^2 - 4ac}}{2a} + \dfrac{-b - \sqrt{b^2 - 4ac}}{2a}$

$= \dfrac{-b + \sqrt{b^2 - 4ac} - b - \sqrt{b^2 - 4ac}}{2a}$

$$= \frac{-b}{a}$$

Products of the roots is $(\frac{-b + \sqrt{b^2 - 4ac}}{2a})(\frac{-b - \sqrt{b^2 - 4ac}}{2a})$

$$= \frac{b^2 - (b^2 - 4ac)}{4a^2}$$

$$= \frac{4ac}{a^2}$$

$$= \frac{c}{a}$$

Examination of the quadratic equation $ax^2 + bx + c = 0$ in the form $x^2 + \frac{b}{a}x + \frac{c}{a} = 0$ shows the coefficient of x to be the sum of the roots with the sign changed, and the absolute term to be the product of the roots. The quadratic equation could be written as $x^2 - $ (sum of roots)x + product of roots = 0.

8. (Supplementary)

(a) The general function and its graph.

(b) An inductive study of the maximum number of roots of a given equation.

(c) The graphical study of equations involving radical signs.

(d) The formation of equations where the roots are the squares of, or the reciprocals of the roots of a given equation.

UNIT 4: THE CIRCLE (6 Weeks)

1. The circle as a set of points equally distant from a fixed point.

The definitions of the following special sets of points associated with the circle: diameter, radius, chord, secant, arc (major and minor) semi circle.

The definitions of special regions associated with the circle: interior, exterior, segment (major and minor), sector

The measures of the circumference, ar length, and areas associated with the circle.

Because of the importance of *patterns* in Geometry, much of

52

the explanations are in the form of type diagrams from which
you should recognize the necessary facts.

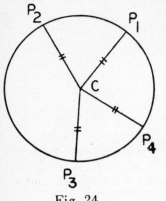

fig 24:
Any points like P_1, P_2, P_3, P_4 that
that lie on the circle are equidistant from the centre, C.

Fig. 24

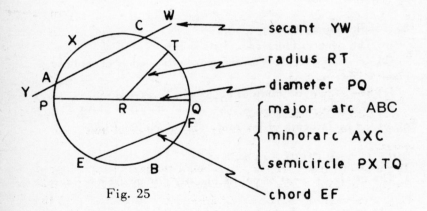

secant YW

radius RT

diameter PQ

major arc ABC

minor arc AXC

semicircle PXTQ

chord EF

Fig. 25

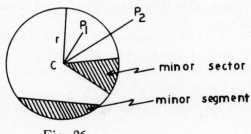

minor sector

minor segment

Fig. 26

In fig. 25, points such as P_1, where $CP_1 < r$, are said to be interior points.

In fig. 26, points such as P_2, where $CP_2 > r$, are said to be exterior points.

Some pertinent formulas
$C = 2\pi r$
$a = r\theta$
$A = \pi r^2$
Area of a sector $= \frac{1}{2}ar$

2. Development of chord properties

(a) **The centre of a circle lies on the right bisector of any chord.**

(b) **The line joining the centre of a circle to the mid point of a chord is perpendicular to the chord.**

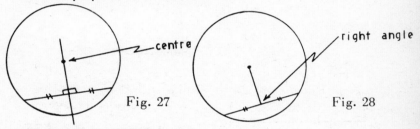

Fig. 27   Fig. 28

(c) **Deductions dealing with**
(i) **the locus of centres of circles passing through two fixed points.**

The type of diagram in fig. 29 is basic to the understanding of the applications of the locus idea involved. Here, C_1C_2 is the line of centres of circles which intersect in B and D. This line is the right bisector of BD. We say that *the locus of the centres of all circles which intersect in two points is the right bisector of the line joining these points.*

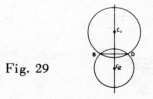

Fig. 29

A type of application is shown in fig. 30. In earlier work in Geometry you had a difficult time showing that AC right bisected BD in the "kite" diagram. Now we can think of A and C as centres of circles intersecting at B and D. Then the *locus*, of which AC is a part, right bisects BD.

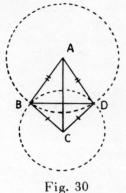

Fig. 30

You should look for other similar applications.

(ii) Circumcircles

The right bisectors of the sides of rectilinear figures with concyclic vertices meet in a point — the centre of the circumscribing circle.

(iii) The relation between distances of chords from the centre and the relative lengths of the chords

In figure 31 AB < AD < AE and CR > CP > 0, where C is the centre of the circle. We conjecture that the closer a chord gets to the centre of the circle, the longer it becomes, the longest chord being the diameter.

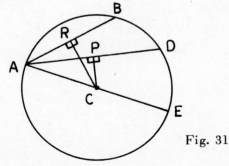

Fig. 31

3. Development of angle propertie s

(a) **Definition of sector angle, an angle inscribed in a circle, and an angle inscribed in a semicircle.**

(b) **An angle inscribed in a circle is equal to one-half of the sector angle subtended by the same arc.**

(c) (i) **angles inscribed in a circle that are subtended by the same arc are equal (and converse)**

  (ii) **an angle inscribed in a semicircle is a right angle (and converse)**

In fig. 32

(i) $\angle$ACB is a sector angle

(ii) $\angle$AEB is an angle inscribed in a circle

(iii) $\angle$GDB is an angle inscribed in a semi circle (GB is a diameter)

(iv) $\angle$ACB = 2$\angle$AFB

  $\angle$ACB = 2$\angle$AEB

  $\therefore$ $\angle$AFB = $\angle$AEB

(v) Becaus e $\angle$GCB = 180°

  $\therefore$ $\angle$GDB = 90° (an angle in a semi circle)

  (iii) **Opposite angles of a quadrilateral inscribed in a circle are supplementary (and converse)**

  (iv) **An exterior angle of a quadrilateral inscribed in a circle is equal to the interior opposite angle (and converse)**

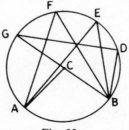

Fig. 32

In fig. 33, $\angle$A + $\angle$C = 180°

  $\angle$B + $\angle$D = 180°

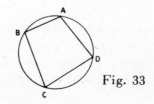

Fig. 33

In fig. 34, $\angle ADE = \angle ABC$

(d) Deductions applying the above properties (including as a deduction the product property of intersecting chords)

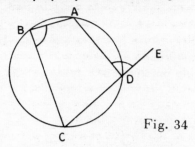

Fig. 34

Given: Two intersecting chords which form by their intersection, the segments a, b, c and d as shown

Prove: $a \cdot b = c \cdot d$

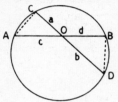

Fig. 35

Proof: Draw the dotted lines as shown
Then $\angle C = \angle B$ (angles on same arc)
      $\angle A = \angle D$ (angles on same arc)
$\therefore \triangle CAD \;|||\; \triangle BDO$ (three angles)
and $a : d = c : b$ (definition of similarity)
which implies $a \cdot b = c \cdot d$ (property of a proportion)

Conclusion: When two chords of a circle intersect, the product of the lengths of the segments of one is equal to the product of the lengths of the segments of the other.

4. Development for *any* curve of the concept of tangent as the limiting position of a secant, and the relation of this concept to the circle.

The tangent at a point P on any curve is the limiting position of a secant PQ as it rotates about P and Q moves along the curve towards P.

5. Development and applications of the tangent properties
   (a) A tangent to a circle is perpendicular to the radius at the point of contact (and converse)

(b) **A line is a tangent to a circle if and only if the distance from the centre of the circle to the line is equal to the radius of the circle.**

(c) **If two tangents are drawn to a circle from an external point, the two tangents are equal, they subtend equal angles at the centre, and they make equal angles with the straight line joining the point to the centre.**

(d) **If a chord and a tangent are drawn through a point on a circle, each of the angles determined by the tangent and the chord is equal to the angle inscribed in the circle on the opposite side of the chord.**

(e) **The square of the length of a tangent from an external point P is equal to the product of the distances from P to the points of intersection of the circle with any secant through P.**

One of the greatest aids in studying Geometry is the recognition of *pattern*. Although much has been done (in man's ingenuity) to develop complicated problems and deductions, basically the use of type diagrams has played a major role in man's understanding of, and reaction to, geometric properties of figures.

As an aid to you we have tested a number of diagrams typical of those you will encounter in your study. You should remember that they may come disguised (compare fig 29-30) but your ability to "see" basic patterns in diagrams presented to you will take you a long way toward the solution of deductions.

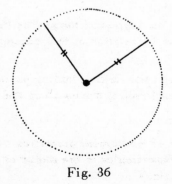 circle as a locus

Fig. 36

58

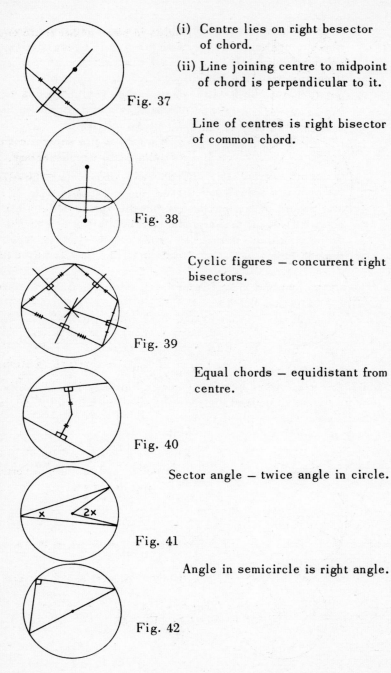

(i) Centre lies on right besector of chord.

(ii) Line joining centre to midpoint of chord is perpendicular to it.

Fig. 37

Line of centres is right bisector of common chord.

Fig. 38

Cyclic figures — concurrent right bisectors.

Fig. 39

Equal chords — equidistant from centre.

Fig. 40

Sector angle — twice angle in circle.

Fig. 41

Angle in semicircle is right angle.

Fig. 42

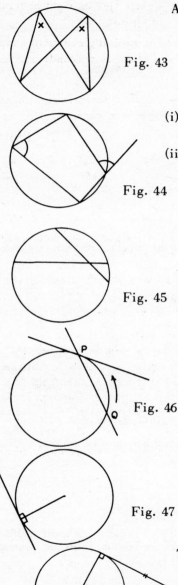

Angles in same segment are equal.

Fig. 43

(i) Opposite angles of cyclic quadrilateral are supplementary.

(ii) Exterior angle equals interior
and opposite angle.

Fig. 44

Products of segments are equal.

Fig. 45

Tangent is limiting position of
secant.

Fig. 46

Tangent and radius are perpendicular at the cirle.

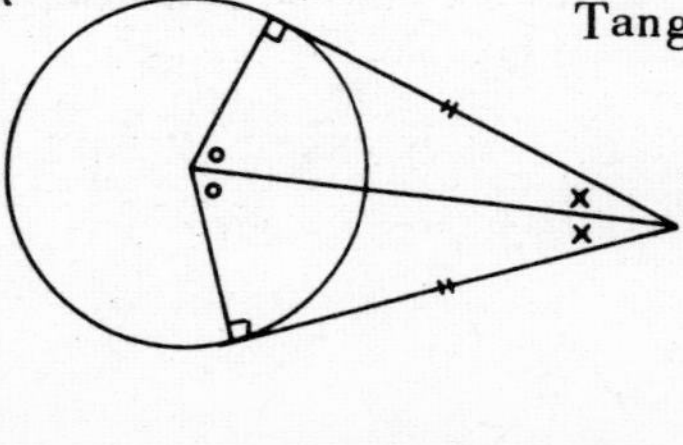

Fig. 47

Tangent properties for the circle.

Fig. 48

60

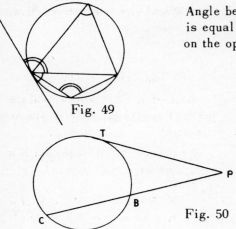

Angle between tangent and chord is equal to angle in the segment on the opposite side of the chord.

Fig. 49

$$\overline{PT}^2 = PB \cdot PC$$

Fig. 50

6. Development of the equation of the circle with radius r and centre (0, 0).

A study of the relation defined by $x^2 + y^2 = r^2$ to establish domain, range, symmetry, intercepts

Regions defined by $x^2 + y^2 < r^2$ and $x^2 + y^2 > r^2$.

The equation $x^2 + y^2 = r^2$ represents the circle with centre (0, 0) and radius r because it may be written in the form $\sqrt{x^2 + y^2} = r$ (using principal roots only) which means that the distance from a moving point (x, y) to a fixed point (0, 0) is a constant, r.

When $x^2 + y^2 = r^2$ is solved for x, it is arranged as $x = \pm\sqrt{r^2 - y^2}$

Note: (i) The number under the radical sign must be positive, or zero.

i.e. $r^2 - y^2 \geq 0$

$y^2 \leq r^2$

$|y| \leq r$ (this is the range)

(ii) for any permissible value of y, there are two values for x which are equal and opposite. (there is symmetry with respect to the y-axis.

When $x^2 + y^2 = r^2$ is solved for y, it is arranged as

$y = \pm\sqrt{r^2 - x^2}$

Note: (i) the number under the radical sign must be positive, or zero.

i.e. $r^2 - x^2 \geq 0$

$x^2 \leq r^2$

$|x| \leq r$ (this is the domain)

(ii) for any permissible value of x, there are two values for y which are equal and opposite. (there is symmetry with respect to the x-axis)

Referring to the form $\sqrt{x^2 + y^2} = r$ it becomes obvious that if a region is defined by $x^2 + y^2 < r^2$, then we may write $\sqrt{x^2 + y^2} < r$, and the region is the interior of the circle.

Referring to the form $\sqrt{x^2 + y^2} = r$ it becomes obvious that if a region is defined by $x^2 + y^2 > r^2$, then we may write $\sqrt{x^2 + y^2} > r$, and the region is the exterior of the circle.

Figure 26 shows the above relationships for points P_1 and P_2 as well as for points on the circle.

7. Analytic proof of particular cases involving the properties indicated in 2(a) and 2(b) above.

8. Finding the length of a tangent from an external point to a circle whose equation is of the form $x^2 + y^2 = 25$. (Particular cases — no proof of general case to be required)

Sample Problem: Find the length of the tangent segment from the point $(-5,3)$ to the circle where equation is $x^2 + y^2 = 16$.

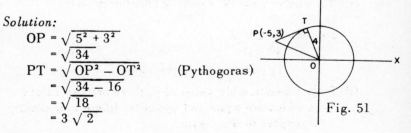

Solution:

OP $= \sqrt{5^2 + 3^2}$

$\quad = \sqrt{34}$

PT $= \sqrt{OP^2 - OT^2}$ (Pythogoras)

$\quad = \sqrt{34 - 16}$

$\quad = \sqrt{18}$

$\quad = 3\sqrt{2}$

Fig. 51

The length of the tangent segment is $3\sqrt{2}$ units.

Note: It is interesting to see that if we arrange the equation

$x^2 + y^2 = 16$ as $x^2 + y^2 - 16 = 0$ and evaluate the *left side* for $x = -5$, $y = 3$, we obtain 18.
$PT = \sqrt{18} = 3\sqrt{2}$. Does this work all the time?

9. Finding the equation of the tangent at a point on a circle whose equation is of the form $x^2 + y^2 = 49$. (Particular cases leading to a recognition of the form of the equation).

By following procedures dependent upon the perpendicularity of radius and tangent at the circle the following table may be drawn up:

Eqn. of Circle	Point on circle	Eqn. of Targent	Adjustment to obtain pattern
$x^2 + y^2 = 25$	$(4,3)$	$4x + 3y = 25$	none
$x^2 + y^2 = 36$	$(4, 2\sqrt{5})$	$4x + 2\sqrt{5}y = 36$	none
$9x^2 + 9y^2 = 37$	$(-2, \frac{1}{3})$	$-18x + 3y = 37$	$-2x + \frac{1}{3}y = \frac{37}{9}$
$16x^2 + 16y^2 = 76$	$(\sqrt{3}/_2, -2)$	$8\sqrt{3}x - 32y = 76$	$\sqrt{3}/_2 x - 2y = \frac{76}{76}$

The pattern appears to be that if the coefficients of x^2 and y^2 are 1 in the original equation then the coefficients of x and y are the respective abscissa and ordinate of the point in the circle, the right member remaining unchanged.

10. (Supplementary)
    Construction of circles given three conditions involving points, lines, and other circles.

UNIT 5: TRIGONOMETRIC FUNCTIONS (3 WEEKS)

1. Review of radian measure

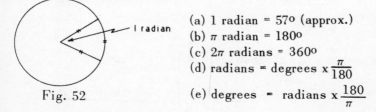

(a) 1 radian = 57° (approx.)
(b) π radian = 180°
(c) 2π radians = 360°
(d) radians = degrees $x \frac{\pi}{180}$
(e) degrees = radians $x \frac{180}{\pi}$

Fig. 52

Review of the general definitions for sin θ, cos θ, and tan θ where $\theta < 2\pi$, and the determination of values in various quadrants.

Steps in determining a ratio of an angle:
1. Choose any point P on the terminal arm
2. Drop a perpendicualr PM on the initial arm
3. From the resulting Δ POM choose the ratios.

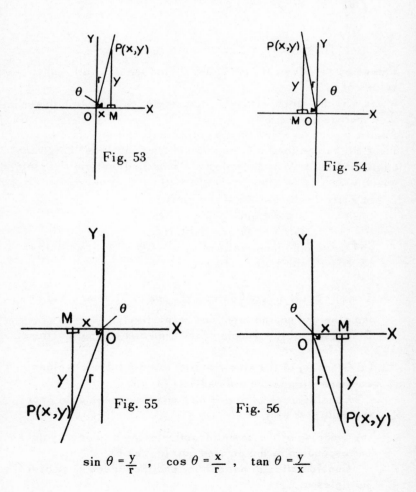

Fig. 53

Fig. 54

Fig. 55

Fig. 56

$$\sin \theta = \frac{y}{r} \quad , \quad \cos \theta = \frac{x}{r} \quad , \quad \tan \theta = \frac{y}{x}$$

64

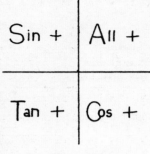

Fig. 57

The CAST rule reviewed.

Extension to values of sin θ, cos θ, and tan θ for all real values of θ.

Where θ is the radian measure of an angle, as the angle increases, so θ increases. $(\theta \in R)$

Angles θ such as π and 3π are coterminal, and therefore have identical values for sin θ, cos θ, and tan θ. Because coterminal angles differ by 2π or multiples of 2π we find that sin θ = sin$(\theta + 2\pi)$, cos θ = cos $(\theta + 2\pi)$, tan θ = tan $(\theta + 2\pi)$.

In general cos θ = cos $(\theta + 2n\pi)$, N$\in$I
                       sin θ = sin $(\theta + 2n\pi)$, N$\in$I
                       tan θ = tan $(\theta + 2n\pi)$, N$\in$I

and these functions (defined by y = cos θ etc.) are said to be *periodic*, with a period of 2π .

2. **The set of all ordered pairs $(\theta, \frac{y}{r})$ and $(\theta, \frac{x}{r})$ determined by the sine and cosine functions respectively.**
   Discussion of the domain of the sine and cosine functions.

3. **(a) Graphing of the sine function using a table of values corresponding to the ordered pair $(\theta,$ sin $\theta)$.**
   Consideration of periodicity and the values at or near the multiples of $\frac{\pi}{2}$.

   (b) Graphing of the cosine function using a table of values corresponding to the ordered pair $(\theta,$ cos $\theta)$.
   Consideration of periodicity and the values at or near the multiples of $\frac{\pi}{2}$.

(c) Consideration of the period and of the amplitude of the sine and cosine functions.

Tables of values:

f: $\theta \to \sin \theta$ ($\theta \epsilon R$)

θ	0	$\frac{\pi}{12}$	$\frac{\pi}{6}$	$\frac{\pi}{4}$	$\frac{\pi}{3}$	$\frac{5\pi}{12}$	$\frac{\pi}{2}$	$\frac{7\pi}{12}$	$\frac{2\pi}{3}$	$\frac{3\pi}{4}$	$\frac{5\pi}{6}$	$\frac{11\pi}{12}$
$\sin \theta$	.0000	.2588	.5000	.7071	.8660	.9659	1.0000	.9659	.8660	.7071	.5000	.2588

θ	π	$\frac{13\pi}{12}$	$\frac{7\pi}{6}$	$\frac{5\pi}{4}$	$\frac{4\pi}{3}$	$\frac{17\pi}{12}$	$\frac{3\pi}{2}$	$\frac{19\pi}{12}$	$\frac{5\pi}{3}$	$\frac{7\pi}{4}$	$\frac{11\pi}{6}$	$\frac{23\pi}{12}$
$\sin \theta$	0	-.2588	-.5000	-.7071	-.8660	-.9659	-1.0000	-.9659	-.8660	-.7071	-.5000	-.2588

θ	2π	$\frac{25\pi}{12}$	$\frac{13\pi}{6}$	$\frac{9\pi}{4}$	$\frac{7\pi}{3}$	$\frac{29\pi}{12}$	$\frac{5\pi}{2}$	$\frac{31\pi}{12}$	$\frac{8\pi}{3}$	$\frac{11\pi}{4}$	$\frac{17\pi}{6}$	$\frac{35\pi}{12}$
$\sin \theta$	.0000	.2588	.5000	.7071	.8660	.9659	1.0000	.9659	.8660	.7071	.5000	.2588

f: $\theta \to \cos \theta$ ($\theta \epsilon R$)

θ	0	$\frac{\pi}{12}$	$\frac{\pi}{6}$	$\frac{\pi}{4}$	$\frac{\pi}{3}$	$\frac{5\pi}{12}$	$\frac{\pi}{2}$	$\frac{7\pi}{12}$	$\frac{2\pi}{3}$	$\frac{3\pi}{4}$	$\frac{5\pi}{6}$	$\frac{11\pi}{12}$
$\cos \theta$	1.0000	.9659	.8660	.7071	.5000	.2588	.0000	-.2588	-.5000	-.7071	-.8660	-.9659

θ	π	$\frac{13\pi}{12}$	$\frac{7\pi}{6}$	$\frac{5\pi}{4}$	$\frac{4\pi}{3}$	$\frac{17\pi}{12}$	$\frac{3\pi}{2}$	$\frac{19\pi}{12}$	$\frac{5\pi}{3}$	$\frac{7\pi}{4}$	$\frac{11\pi}{6}$	$\frac{23\pi}{12}$
$\cos \theta$	-1.000	-.9659	-.8660	-.7071	-.5000	-.2588	.0000	.2588	.5000	.7071	.8660	.9659

θ	2π	$\frac{25\pi}{12}$	$\frac{13\pi}{6}$	$\frac{9\pi}{4}$	$\frac{7\pi}{3}$	$\frac{29\pi}{12}$	$\frac{5\pi}{2}$	$\frac{31\pi}{12}$	$\frac{8\pi}{3}$	$\frac{11\pi}{4}$	$\frac{17\pi}{6}$	$\frac{35\pi}{12}$
$\cos \theta$	1.0000	.9659	.8660	.7071	.5000	.2588	.0000	-.2588	-.5000	-.7071	-.8660	-.9659

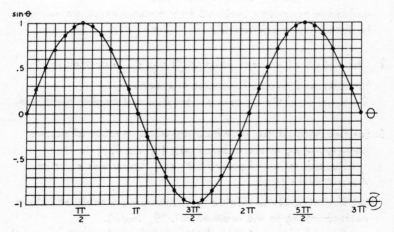

Fig. 58

66

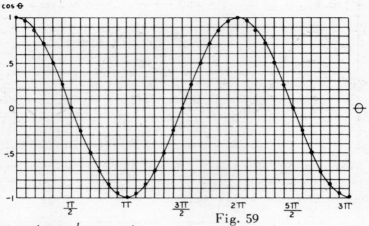

Fig. 59

Some notes and comments:

1. Amplitude is 1 (thus the range is from –1 to +1 inclusive)
2. A repetition of the pattern shown by fig. 58–59 indicate a *period* of 2π.
3. The domain is R, because θ can take on any real values for real sin θ or cos θ, and the range = $\{y \mid -1 \le y \le 1, y \in r\}$
4. Examine the table of values, and memorize values of sin θ and cos θ for $\theta = 0, \dfrac{\pi}{2}, \dfrac{\pi}{3}, \pi, 2\pi$ and others that you may find used frequently.
5. Fig. 58–59 show graphically the relationship between the two curves. There is a *phase difference* between the curves of $\dfrac{\pi}{2}$.
6. You should graph these curves carefully (for your own edification!). Now that this has been done your main concern should be with regard to *behaviour* of the curve. When you plot sine and cosine curves, plot only the values showing zero points, crests and troughs. Join these points carefully with a *smooth curve* to obtain the required shape.

4. (a) Graphing of the function defined by y = a sin θ (where a is positive) to show the effect on the amplitude when a is (i) equal to 1, (ii) less than 1, (iii) greater than 1.

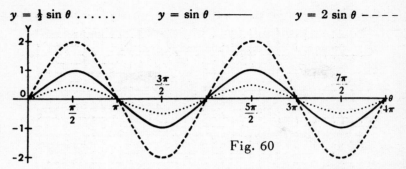

$$y = \tfrac{1}{2}\sin\theta \ldots\ldots \qquad y = \sin\theta \text{——} \qquad y = 2\sin\theta \text{- - - -}$$

Fig. 60

The amplitude increases as the coefficient of $\sin\theta$ increases. In fact, the coefficient *is* the amplitude when the defining sentence is written in this form.

(b) Graphing of the function defined by y = sin k θ, where k is positive, to show that k changes the period of the curve, but not the amplitude.

$$y = \sin\tfrac{1}{2}\theta \ldots\ldots\ldots$$
$$y = \sin\theta \text{————}$$
$$y = \sin 2\theta \text{- - - - - - -}$$

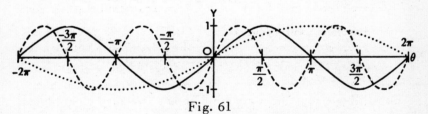

Fig. 61

The period decreases as the coefficient of θ increases.

(c) Graphing of the function defined by y = a sin k θ, where a and k are positive, to show the combined results of a change of the amplitude and of the period.

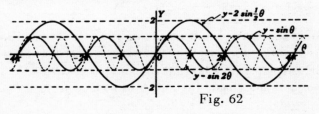

Fig. 62

(d) Graphing of the function defined by y = a sin (θ + d), where *a* **is positive and d is real, to show the combined results of a change of the amplitude and the phase.**

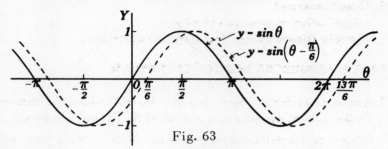

Fig. 63

If d is positive then y = sin θ and y = sin (θ + d) represent curves that are d units "apart" on the θ scale, the latter being shifted to the left.

(e) Graphical determination of the relation between the sine and cosine functions of θ **and** θ + $\frac{\pi}{2}$**.**

An examination of the graphs if fig. 58—59 showns that the cosine curve is shifted $\frac{\pi}{2}$ units to the left. The shift to the right could be made by plotting the graph of the function defined by y = cos (θ − $\frac{\pi}{2}$.)

You should examine other combinations which would place these curves in phase, 90º out of phase, or 180º out of phase. You will be conducting a study which has intrigued electricians and electrical engineers for decades.

5. Proof of the sine law and cosine law.

Sine Law $\quad \dfrac{a}{\sin A} = \dfrac{b}{\sin B} = \dfrac{c}{\sin C}$

Cosine Law $\quad a^2 = b^2 + c^2 - 2bc \cos A$
$\qquad\qquad\quad b^2 = a^2 + c^2 - 2ac \cos B$
$\qquad\qquad\quad c^2 = a^2 + b^2 - 2ab \cos C$

Problems using the sine and cosine laws restricted to cases where numbers are simple (using tables of four decimal figures

for one - degree intervals and angles to the nearest degree).
Use of the approximation sign.

6. (Supplementary)
    Application to angular velocity
    Sample trigonometric identities and equations.

UNIT 6: SEQUENCES AND SERIES (3 WEEKS)

1. Sequence is defined by means of a function where the domain
    is the natural numbers or a subset of the natural numbers.

    $f: x \to 2x + 1$ defines a sequence in which $x \in N$ (or preferably
    $+ I$).
    f defines { (1,3), (2,5), 3,7) , (4,9) . . . } which are ordered
    pairs. The second element of the ordered pair is frequently
    called a *term* of the sequence. Thus 3,5,7,9, . . . are four
    terms of the sequence.

    Distinction between a finite and infinite sequence.
    Terms of a sequence.
    General term of a sequence.
    In the sequence $f: x \to 2x + 1$ if the values of x are limited to
    a proper subset of N or $+I$ then the sequence is finite.
    Example: List the terms of the ten term sequence 2,7,12,17 . . .
    Solution: the sequence is 2,7,12,17,22,27,32,37,42,47.

    On the other hand in many cases no upper limit is placed on
    x. Such a series is infinite.

    The general term is usually defined in terms of the term
    number. Thus the general term of $f: x \to 2x + 1$ is $2x + 1$. Sometimes
    it is useful to insert a general term within a sequence. For
    example the second elements of the set of ordered pairs (1,3),
    (2,5), (3,7) . . . form an ordered set of numbers which may be
    written 3,5,7,9, . . . $2x + 1$, . . . 61,63, . . .

    Particular sequences defined by
        (i) function notation

Examples: (a) f = { (x,y) | y = 3x − 2, x ϵ + I}

      (b) f: n → 4n + 3

(ii) the first few terms and the general term.

Example: In the series 10,13,16, . . . 3n + 7 find the tenth term, and the sum of the first five terms.

(iii) The general term only.

Example: Write the first four terms of the sequence whose general term is x − 7.

(iv) a recursion formula.

Example: List the sixth and seventh terms of the sequence in which t_1 = 1, t_2 = 1, t_k = t_{k-1} + 3.

Note that in this example at least one term had to be given, and that extra terms *could* be present (example t_1) which were "beyond" the requirements of the definition.

2. Definition of arithmetic and geometric sequences the general arithmetic and the general geometric sequences.

    An arithmetic sequences is one defined by a linear relation. It is found on investigation that this also results in any term being found by adding a fixed quantity (the common difference) to the previous term.

    The general arithmetic sequence is a, a + d, a + 2d, a + 3d, . . . a + (n − 1) d, . . .

    The geometric sequence is defined by an exponential relation, eg. y = 3^x (x ϵ +I). It is found on investigation, that this also results in any term being found by multiplying the previous term by a fixed quantity (the common ratio.)

    The general arithmetic sequence is a, ar^2, ar^3, . . . ar^n, . . .

3. Definition of a series

Inductive discovery of the sum of a finite number of terms of a particular series.

The sum of n terms of the general arithmetic and the general geometric series.

    A series is an indicated sum of the terms of a sequence. Eg. 3,5,7,9 is a sequence; 3+5+7+9 is a series; 24 is the sum of the series.

    It is difficult to suggest methods of studying an inductive

approach. In the main they rely on the use of trial and error until a workable system finally evolves.

Consider the series $3+8+13+18+23+28$ whose sum we would like to know. It is fine to add the terms up and obtain a result, but is interesting to see that (a) $t_1 + t_2 = 11$ and also

$$\frac{(3+8)}{2}\, 2 = 11$$

(b) $t_1 + t_2 + t_3 = 24$

$$\frac{(3+13)}{2}\, 3 = 24$$

(c) $t_1 + t_2 + t_3 + t_4 = 42$ and also

$$\frac{(3+18)}{2}\, 4 = 42$$

The above method of averaging came as the result of trial and error. This takes time, but is intriguing and rewarding.

*Can you find other ways of summing the above series?

Sum of general arithmetic series is

$$\frac{n}{2}\,[2a + (n - 1)\, d]$$

Sum of general geometric series is

$$\frac{a\,(1-r^n)}{1-r},\ r = 1 \text{ or } \frac{a\,(r^n-1)}{r-1},\ r \neq 1$$

*a = common difference, r = common ratio, n = number of terms

4. Introduction to annuities
   Amount and present value of annuities

5. (Supplementary)
   Mathematical induction.

SAMPLE CHRISTMAS EXAMINATION (1½ hr.)

1. (a) Draw the following lines, using one pair of axes:
   (i) $2x + y = 6$
   (ii) $2x + y = 2$
   (iii) $2x + y = 4$
   (iv) $2x + y = 0$
   These lines belong to the same family of lines. How are they related? Write an equation which represents the complete family.

Solution:
    All lines have the same slope
    and are parallel.
    The equation 2x + y = b
    represents all members of the
    family.

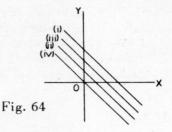

Fig. 64

1. (b) Find b so that $3x - y - 2 = 0$, $2x + y + 1 = 0$,
    $bx + y + 3 = 0$ represent concurrent lines.

Solution:
    Solve $3x - y = 2$ (1)
             $2x + y = -1$ (2)
    _____
                $x = \frac{1}{5}$
                $y = -\frac{7}{5}$
    If the lines are concurrent, then the point $(\frac{1}{5}, -\frac{7}{5})$ must
satisfy the equation $bx + y + 3 = 0$
                i.e. $b = -8$

2. (a) Evaluate $(9.129)^{\frac{3}{4}}$
    Solution: let $x = (9.129)^{\frac{3}{4}}$

$$\begin{array}{l} \log 9.120 = 0.9604 \\ \quad\quad 4)\ .9604 \\ \quad\quad \overline{0.2401} \\ \frac{3}{4} \log 9.129 = 0.7203 \end{array}$$

            $x = 5.251$

2. (b) Evaluate and write the answer in standard form
    $(1.37 \times 10^{23}) \div (1.5 \times 10^{11})$.
Solution: $\dfrac{1.37 \times 10^{23}}{1.5 \times 10^{11}}$
    $= .913 \times 10^{12}$
    $= 9.1 \times 10^{11}$

3. A house is purchased by paying $5000 now and $4000 at the
    end of one year. If the rate of interest is 5% compounded
    semi-annually, what is the equivalent cash price of the house?

Solution:

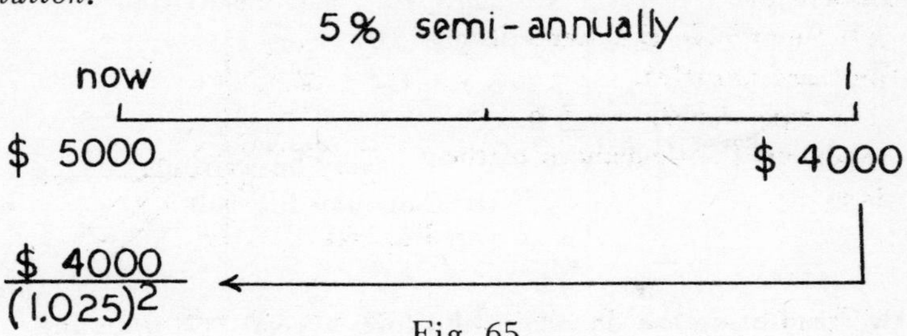

5% semi-annually

now

$ 5000 $ 4000

$$\frac{\$\ 4000}{(1.025)^2}$$

Fig. 65

$$P.V. = 5000 + \frac{4000}{(1.025)^2}$$

$$= 5000 = 4000\ (0.95181)$$
$$= 5000 + 3807.24$$
$$= 8807.24$$

The equivalent cash value is $8807.24

4. Fill in the blanks:
   (a) $\log_2 32$ = _____
   (b) $\log_6 \sqrt{6}$ = _____
   (c) $\log_a 1$ = _____
   (d) $\log_{10} 10^{1.7}$ = _____
   (e) $10^{\log^{100}}$ = _____

Solution:

(a) $\log_2 32 = 5$
$\qquad$ a = log 32 in exponential form
$\qquad$ may be written $32 = 2^a$
$\qquad\qquad$ but $32 = 2^5$
$\qquad\qquad \therefore\ a = 5$

(b) $\log_6 \sqrt{6} = \frac{1}{2}$
$\qquad$ a = $\log_6 \sqrt{6}$ in exponential form
$\qquad$ may be written $6^a = \sqrt{6}$
$\qquad\qquad$ but $\sqrt{6} = 6^{\frac{1}{2}}$
$\qquad\qquad \therefore a = \frac{1}{2}$

(c) $\log_a 1 = 0$
$\qquad$ b = $\log_a 1$ may be written
$\qquad$ $1 = a^b$
$\qquad \therefore\ b = 0$

74

(d) $\log_{10} 10^{1.7} = 1.7$ $\begin{array}{l} y = \log_{10} 10^{1.7} \text{ may be written} \\ \quad 10^{1.7} = 10^y \\ \therefore\ y = 1.7 \end{array}$

(e) $10^{\log^{100}} = 100$ $\begin{array}{l} y = 10^{\log^{100}} \text{ may be written} \\ y = 10^2 \ (\text{because } \log 100 = 2) \\ \quad = 100 \end{array}$

5. By completing the square in the form $a(x-m)^2 + d$ draw the graph of the function defined by f: $x \to x^2 - 5x + 7$. State the range of the function.

Solution: $f = x^2 - 5x + 7$
$$= x^2 - 5x + \frac{25}{4} + 7 - \frac{25}{4}$$
$$= (x - \frac{5}{2})^2 + \tfrac{3}{4}$$

The range is ¾ and all real numbers greater than ¾.

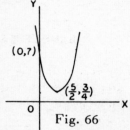

Fig. 66

6. A particle falls $16t^2$ feet through the atmosphere in t seconds. Draw the graph of the relation which determines the set $\{(t,d) \mid d = 16t^2;\ 0 \le t \le 5,\ t \epsilon R\}$

(a) Is this relation a funtion? Explain.
(b) From the graph, estimate the number of feet which a particle falls in 3½ seconds.
(c) From the graph, estimate how lon it would take a particle to fall 81 feet.

Solution:

Table of values $d = 16t^2$

t	0	1	2	3	4	5
d	0	16	64	144	250	400

(a) The relation is a function because no two ordered pairs have the same first element.
(b) 196 ft.

(c) ⁹⁄₄ sec.

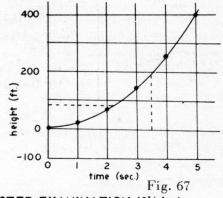

Fig. 67

SAMPLE EASTER EXAMINATION (1½ hr.)

1. By completing the square in the form a $(x - m)^2 + d$ draw the graph of the function defined by f: $x \to 5x^2 + 10x + 3$. State the range of the function.

Solution:

$$f = 5x^2 + 10x + 3$$
$$= 5(x^2 + 2x) + 3$$
$$= 5(x^2 + 2x + 1) + 3 - 5$$
$$= 5(x + 1)^2 - 2$$

The range is –2 and all real numbers greater than –2.

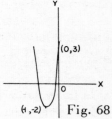

Fig. 68

2. DB is a tangent segment and DCA is a secant from a point D to a circle, centre O. Prove that ΔBCD is similar to ΔABD.

Solution:

Given: DB is a tangent segment
              DCA is a secant from D

Prove: ΔBCD ||| ΔABD

Prof: In ΔBCD and ΔBAD
            ∠ D is common

            ∠ DBC = ∠ BAC (Angle between chord and tangent)

∴   ∠ BCD = ∠ ABD (Angle sum triangle)

∴   ΔBCD ||| ΔBAD (3 angles)

76

3. A trust fund is set up to provide a boy with $10,000 on his twenty-first birthday. If it is agreed that he receive the money on his eighteenth birthday, and the interest rate is 4% compounded semi-annually, how much will he receive?

Solution:

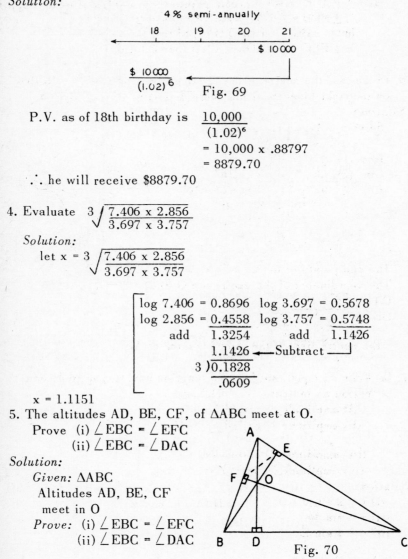

4 % semi-annually

Fig. 69

P.V. as of 18th birthday is $\dfrac{10,000}{(1.02)^6}$

= 10,000 x .88797

= 8879.70

∴ he will receive $8879.70

4. Evaluate $3\sqrt{\dfrac{7.406 \times 2.856}{3.697 \times 3.757}}$

Solution:

let x = $3\sqrt{\dfrac{7.406 \times 2.856}{3.697 \times 3.757}}$

log 7.406 = 0.8696	log 3.697 = 0.5678
log 2.856 = 0.4558	log 3.757 = 0.5748
add 1.3254	add 1.1426
1.1426 ← Subtract ⎦	
3)0.1828	
.0609	

x = 1.1151

5. The altitudes AD, BE, CF, of ΔABC meet at O.

Prove (i) ∠EBC = ∠EFC
　　　 (ii) ∠EBC = ∠DAC

Solution:

Given: ΔABC

Altitudes AD, BE, CF
meet in O

Prove: (i) ∠EBC = ∠EFC
　　　　 (ii) ∠EBC = ∠DAC

Fig. 70

Page 77

Proof:
(i) B,C,E,F are concyclic points (equal angles on same side of common line)
∴ ∠EBC = ∠EFC (Angles in same segment)
(ii) A,F,D,E, are concyclic points (opp. angles of quad. supp.)
∴ ∠EFD = ∠EAO (Angles in same segment)
but ∠EBC = ∠LEFO (Proved in (i))
∴ ∠EBC = ∠EAO = ∠CAD (Substitution)

6. Prove that the centre of the circle defined by $x^2 + y^2 = 16$ lies on the right bisecter of the chord determined by $x - 3y = 4$.

Solution:

Solve $x - 3y = 4$ (1)
$x^2 + y^2 = 16$ (2)
from (1) $x = 3y + 4$
in (2) $(3y + 4)^2 + y^2 = 16$
i.e. $9y^2 + 24y + 16 + y^2 = 16$
$10y^2 + 24y = 0$
$y(5y + 12) = 0$
$y = 0$ or $-\frac{12}{5}$
∴ $x = 4$ or $-\frac{16}{5}$

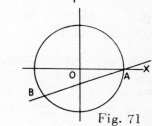
Fig. 71

The end points of the chord are A (400) and B ($-\frac{16}{5}, -\frac{12}{5}$)
The coordinates of the centre are O (0,0)
$OA = \sqrt{16} = 4$
$OB = \sqrt{(\frac{16}{5})^2 + (\frac{12}{5})^2} = 4$
∴ the centre lies on the right bisecter of AB.

7. (a) *Write* an equation of a sine function having amplitude and period as indicated in each case:
(i) amplitude 2; period 2π.
(ii) amplitude 1; period $\frac{\pi}{2}$.
(iii) amplitude 4; period 4π.
(iv) amplitude ½; period 3π.

Solution:
(i) $y = 2 \sin \theta$
(ii) $y = \sin 4\theta$
(iii) $y = 4 \sin \frac{\theta}{2}$
(iv) $y = \frac{1}{2} \sin \frac{2\pi}{3}$

for an explanation of the coefficients be sure to examine figures 60,61,62.

7. (b) If x = 110 sin 120 πt represents the voltage of an alternating current, state the amplitude and period of the voltage.

Solution:

The amplitude is the coefficient of sin θ,
i.e. 110.

The period is 2π times the reciprocal of the coefficient of t,
i.e. $2\pi \left(\dfrac{1}{120 \pi} \right) = \dfrac{1}{60}$.

SAMPLE JUNE EXAMINATION (1½ hr.)

1. Graph the system $x - 1 \leq y \leq x + 1$

Solution: The inequations are written so that they mean
$y \leq x + 1$ and $y \geq x - 1$.

Table of values for y = x + 1

x	0	2
y	1	3

Table of values for y = x - 1

x	0	2
y	-1	1

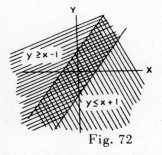

Fig. 72

2. Two circles are tangent to the same line at A and have centres on opposite sides of the line. X,C are points of one circle such that X,A,Y are collinear, and C,A,D are collinear. Prove $\angle$ XCA = $\angle$ YDA.

Solution:

Given: Two circles touching a
common line at A
XAY and CAD are chords

of the circles such that
X,A,Y, and C,A,D, are
two sets of collinear points.

Prove: $\angle XCA = \angle YDA$

Proof:

$\angle PAX = \angle XCA$ (angle between chord and tangent)

$\angle TAY = \angle ADY$ (angle between chord and tangent)

but $\angle PAX = \angle TAY$ (opposite angles)

$\therefore \angle XCA = \angle ADY$ (Substitution)

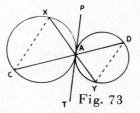

Fig. 73

3. If energy and mass are related by the equation $E = mc^2$, where c is the velocity of light (3.00×10^{10} cm./sec.), find the energy available in a mass of 3 grams. (The unit of energy in this case would be *ergs*)

Solution:

   when $m = 3$, $c = 3.00 \times 10^{10}$

$$E = mc^2$$
$$= 3 \ (3.00 \times 10^{10})^2$$
$$= 27 \times 10^{20}$$
$$= 2.7 \times 10^{21}$$

The energy is 2.7×10^{21} ergs.

4. (a) For a certain arithmetic series $t_5 = 16$ and $S_{20} = 650$. Find a and d.

Solution: If $t_5 = 16$

   Then $a + 4d = 16$. (1)

   If $S_{20} = 650$

   Then $\dfrac{20}{2} [2a + (20 - 1) d] = 650$

   i.e. $10 [2a + 19d] = 650$ (2)

   rewrite (2) $2a + 19d = 65$

   (1) x 2 $2a + 8d = 32$

   Subtract $\overline{11d = 33}$

$$d = 3$$
$$\therefore \quad a = 4$$

which are the required values.

4. (b) The value of a certain type of car depreciates 20% in the first year and 5% each year afterwards. Find the value of a 5 year old car of this type which originally sold for $4000.

Solution I:

The value is 4000 x 8 x (.95)⁴

$$
\begin{aligned}
&\begin{bmatrix}
\log 4000 &= 3.6021 \\
\log .8 &= \overline{1}.9031 \\
4 \log .95 &= \overline{1}.9108 \\
\text{add} &\quad 3.4160
\end{bmatrix}
\end{aligned}
$$

= 2606

∴ the car's value is $2606

Solution II:

$$4000 \times .2 = 800$$
$$(4000 - 800) \times .05 = 160$$
$$(3200 - 160) \times .05 = 152$$
$$(3040 - 152) \times .05 = 144.4$$
$$(2888 - 144.4) \times .05 = 137.18$$

The value of the car is $(2743.6 - 137.18) = $2606.42

i.e. $2606 to the nearest dollar.

5. Find the nature of the roots in each of the following equations:

(a) $2x^2 + \sqrt{8}\,x + 1 = 0$

(b) $\sqrt{3}\,x^2 + x - 2\sqrt{3} = 0$

(c) $3x^2 + \sqrt{5}\,x - 1 = 0$

Solution:

(a) In $2x^2 + \sqrt{8}\,x + 1 = 0$

$$D = 8 - 8 = 0$$

∴ The roots are real and equal

(b) In $\sqrt{3}\,x^2 + x - 2\sqrt{3} = 0$

$$D = 1 + 24 = 25$$

∴ The roots are real and unequal.

(c) In $3x^2 + \sqrt{5}\,x - 1 = 0$

$$D = 5 + 12 = 12$$

∴ The roots are real and unequal.

6. On a 360 yard golf hole a golfer drives 200 yards, but 25º off
   line. If he hits the ball 160 yards directly towards the hole
   in his second shot, how far from the hole will he be?
Solution:

Disregard the 160 yard
measurement in fig. 74
and calculate the length of
AC.

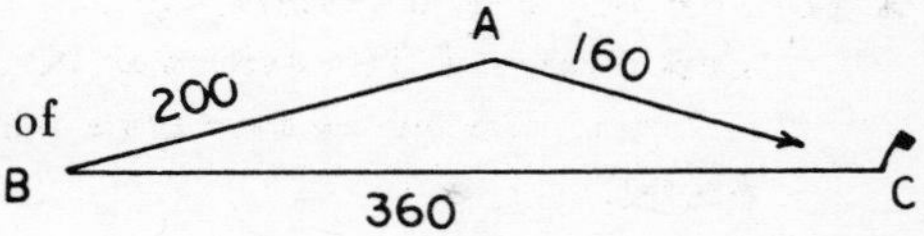

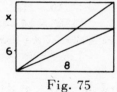

Fig. 74

By the cosine law

$$b^2 = a^2 + c^2 - 2ac \cos B$$
$$= 360^2 + 200^2 - 2(360)(200) \cos 25º$$
$$= 39,093$$
$$b = \sqrt{39,093} \text{ taking the positive root only}$$
$$= 197 \text{ approx.}$$

The golfer is 197 – 160 = 37 yards from the hole.

7. How much must be added to the height of a rectangle 8 inches
   long and 6 inches high in order to form a new rectangle whose
   diagonal is 7 inches longer than the diagonal of the original
   rectangle?
Solution:

Let the measure in inches of
the amount added to the height
be x (where $x \in +R$)

Fig. 75

The original diagonal had a length of $\sqrt{36 + 64} = 10$
∴ the final diagonal has a length of 17.
hence $\sqrt{(6 + x)^2 + 8^2} = 17$

$$36 + 12x + x^2 + 64 = 289$$
$$x^2 + 12x - 189 = 0$$
$$(x + 21)(x - 9) = 0$$
$$x = -24 \text{ or } 9$$

∴ the amount added is 9 inches.
(Note the restriction placed on the domain).

NOTES

NOTES

NOTES

NOTES

NOTES

NOTES

NOTES

NOTES

NOTES

NOTES

NOTES